THE PAN HANDLE

*Prominent parts
from Britain's most
outstanding organ.*

Featuring material first published
in Viz magazine issues 53 to 57.

Edited by Chris Donald
Written and illustrated by
Chris Donald, Graham Dury, Simon Thorp and Simon Donald

With contributions from
Davey Jones and John Fardell
Photography by Colin Davison

ISBN 870870 492

Published in Great Britain by John Brown Publishing Limited,
The Boathouse, Crabtree Lane, Fulham, London SW6 6LU.

First printing September 1994.
Second printing April 1995.

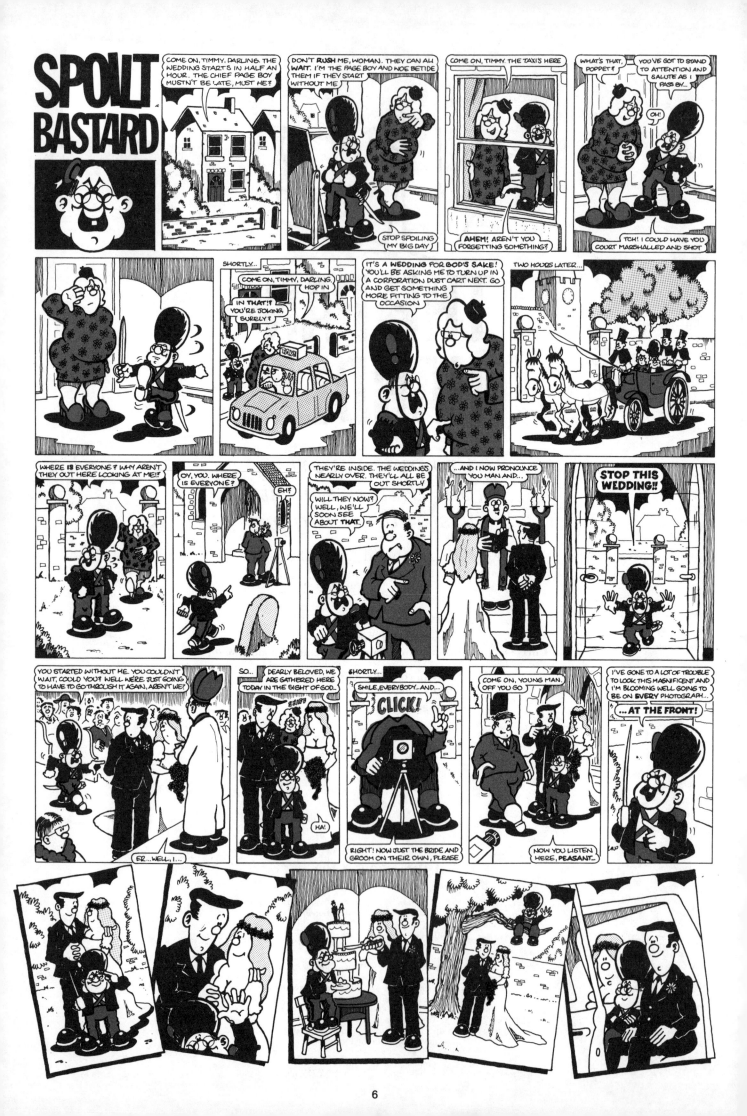

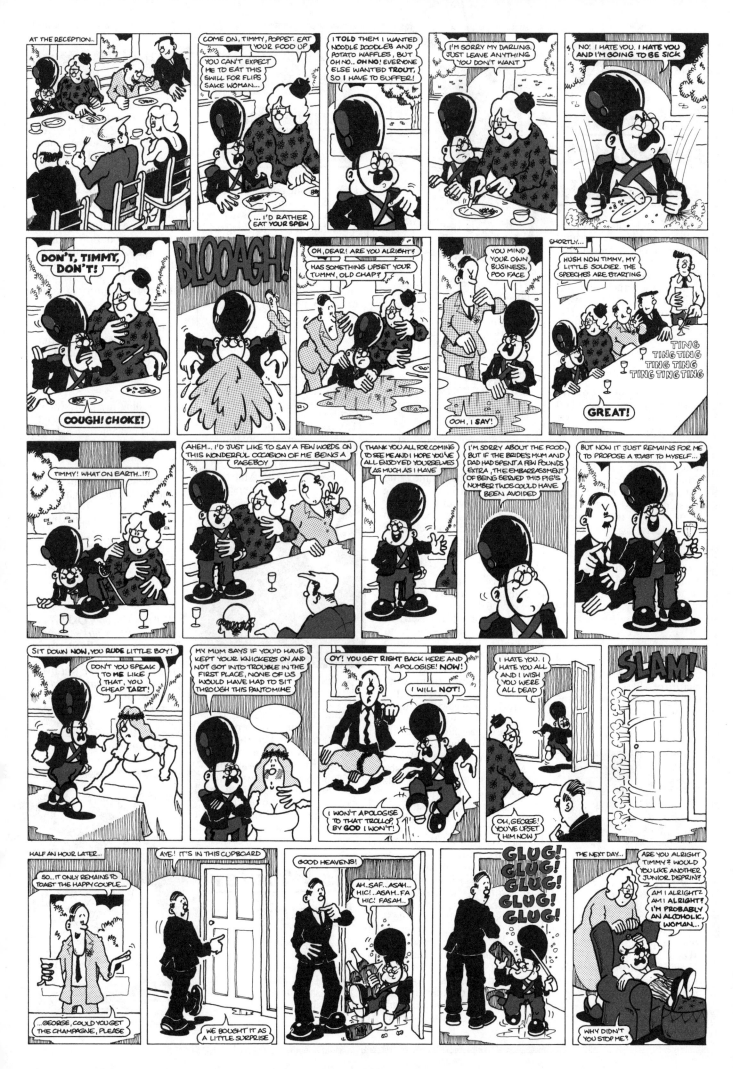

LETTERBOX

This rude spaghetti is 'pasta' joke

LetterBocks
Viz Commick
P.O. Box 1 PT
Newcasle upon Tyne
NE99 1PT

After buying a tin of 'Alphabetti Spagetti' I was horrified to find that by arranging the letters on the side of my plate, not only was I able to spell the word 'fuck', but also 'shit' and 'wank' as well. Surely our children should be protected from such filth. How do other readers feel?

Mrs J. Blackford
Eversham

My false teeth hurt for forty years until last summer when my husband and I went on holiday to Corfu. I explained the problem to another lady who was staying at the same hotel, and she said she had similar problems. It turned out that we had both visited the same dentist to have false teeth fitted on the same day forty years ago, and the dentist had given us both the wrong teeth by mistake. We swapped teeth and hey presto! We both had a perfect fit. We spent the rest of our holiday smiling, and we still keep in touch regularly.

Mrs Edna Beadbath
Bath

How about reprinting that picture of a bloke kissing that bird's arse. I missed it the first time round.

R. S. Wood
Fleetwood

*Here's that picture one more time, especially for you Mr Wood.
Would any other readers like us to reprint once again anything that we have used several times already? Write to 'Memories' at our usual address.

They say the best things in life are free. Well on Friday I had ten pints of lager and a chicken madras, and it cost me twenty-four quid.

M. Ireland
Leamington Spa

Boxing clever

I wish people would stop criticising boxing. It's a healthy sport which teaches youngsters discipline and respect. Without boxing these kids would probably end up punching people in the street, shooting people or raping women.

J. London
London

Twenty years ago my daughter who had prominent ears, buck teeth and wore thick spectacles, used to constantly come home from school crying after being picked on by the other children for being ugly. I told her to ignore them, and remember the story of the ugly duckling who grew up to be a beautiful swan.
Twenty years later and I still wonder whether this would have been the case with her. Alas I'll never know as she hung herself in the bicycle sheds during her third year.

Mr H. Chesterfield
Chesterfield

The other day a BBC weatherman made a hilarious gaffe. Having replaced a map of the British Isles with one of Europe, he boldly announced "This shows the weather on a larger scale". Clearly this was incorrect, as despite the map showing a *larger land area*, the *scale* was in fact *smaller*. How we laughed as he carried on with his forecast, completely oblivious of his comical blunder.

C. Johnston-Brady
Falkirk

Name that tune in one

I've got a tune going round in my head and for the life of me I can't remember what it's called. It goes *da da di da da dum da da da dee.* Then it goes *da doom doom doobi doom. B-dap b-dap b-dap.* Maybe one of your readers could name that tune and put me out of my misery.

W. Heldnop
Clapham

When my wife rang me at work the other day and said the alarm had gone off I immediately rushed home. Little did I know she was in fact refering to the pop group The Alarm. "They haven't made a decent record since 68 Guns", she told me as I walked in the door.

R. Mattress
Hersham

The Alarm

The vast majority of road traffic accidents happen within three miles of the driver's home. I therefore reduce my risk of crashing by keeping my car in a lock-up garage three miles away, and travelling to and from the garage by bicycle. Once in my car I can drive recklessly as I like with little or no danger of crashing.

D. Turner
Canterbury

No Wonder I laugh

I'm completely deaf, but I love to listen to Stevie Wonder records – because he's *blind!* How the staff at the HMV shop laugh when I tell them what I'm up to!

Andy Tipper
Edgbaston

I'll vote for the first political party who send me £25.

B. Leicester
57 Acacia Avenue
Fulchester

One way to beat the budget blues, impress the women *and* your neighbours is to toddle down to your local hardware store and spend all your money on tools, fixings and other D.I.Y. products for your home. Buying now will save you pounds, and will probably improve your sex life.

G. Clark
Clark's Tools & Hardware
Market Hall, Hull
'Ironmongers to the old town for over 50 years. Open six days a week'

I was telling my wife how it seems like only yesterday I sat and watched England beat Germany in the World Cup Final. I felt a proper fool when she reminded me that I'd watched the match on video the previous night.

D. Turner
Canterbury

I live in Shirley. Do any other readers live in a place with a girl's name?

R. J. Plester
Shirley

Well readers, do **YOU live in a place with a girl's name? Perhaps you live in a place called Doris, or Samantha. Or Maureen. Wherever you live, if its got a girl's name, we want to know. Write to us at our Letterbocks address, and mark your envelopes 'Girls' Names'. We might send you a prize or something.*

IT'S MADNESS GOING TO SEA IN WEATHER LIKE THIS

I'VE BEEN DRIVING IN MY CAR. IT ISN'T QUITE A JAG-U-AR...

You can hassle ginger people as much as you like, it doesn't bother me. I've got ginger hair, I'm hung like a horse and all the birds fancy me. So fuck you.

Rob Wales

Let's spice up our cash

As a loyal British citizen I'm all for having a picture of a Royal on our bank notes, but does it *have* to be the Queen. After all, she is getting on a bit.

Why can't we have a picture of Lady Di (preferably in her bikini) or Lady Helen 'Melons' Windsor? And why have farts like Shakespeare and George Stephenson on the back? What's wrong with Samantha Fox, or the lovely Linda Lucardi? You never know, it might even encourage people to save a bit.

Elvis Mearns
Heston

Melons Windsor

I'm fed up with these 'Keep Sunday Special' campaigners who moan about new Sunday trading laws. They should all have big yellow crosses painted on their backs, and if one of them so much as nips out to buy a paper on a Sunday morning, other people should stone them.

Let's put an end to this hypocrisy.

Geoffrey Widdle
Swansea

FELLAS. Keep wives and girlfriends on their toes by murmering the names of other women whilst pretending to be asleep.

R. J. Gillon
Coventry

WHEN boiling an egg in the morning save time by popping a teabag and a drop of milk into the pan. Hey presto! – a boiled egg and a cup of tea.

Haplay Lloyd
Runcorn

LADIES. Don't splash out on expensive nail files. Make your own by sticking the sides of matchboxes to an old lollipop stick.

Ann Wilson
Preston

WHEN it stops raining go to the nearest car park. By observing the number of dry patches you can work out exactly how many cars have left the car park since the rain stopped.

H. Dingle
London

GARDENERS. Avoid back-ache from bending to pick your tomatoes. Simply dig a trench four feet deep alongside your plants. Step into the trench and – hey presto! Your tomatoes are at chest height.

John Tagliarini
Sicily

STOP being scared of spiders by handling spiders on a regular basis until you aren't scared of spiders anymore.

Mrs Nan Chester
Manchester

SAVE on booze by drinking cold tea instead of whisky. The following morning you can create the effects of a hang-over by drinking a thimble full of washing up liquid and banging your head repeatedly on a wall.

F. Horton
Chipping Norton

PRETEND your car has central locking by leaving all the doors unlocked except the driver's door. When you return, unlock the drivers door and – hey presto! All the doors are unlocked.

Tom Bradley
Heaton

CONVINCE your neighbours that you have fluorescent strip lights in your bedroom by rapidly flicking the switch on and off for a few moments every evening before you enter the room.

Mike Millar
Glasgow

AVOID dirty finger marks around light switches by fixing an ordinary bathroom soap dish and a glass holder by the side of each switch. Guests can then use the soap and water from the glass to wash their hands before touching the switch. Oh, and you'll need a small towel rail too.

Mrs M. Head
Willenhall

HELP the Samaritans by sending them problem pages cut out of old magazines. They will then be in a position to help if they encounter any similar problems themselves.

S. Coulton
Sefton

KEEP your kids amused on shopping trips by giving them 3 wooden balls each and offering a goldfish to the first one who can knock a passer-by's hat off.

Hapag Lloyd
Runcorn

PLANT POTTY

How about this for the latest fad in America.

Believe it or not crazy Californians are forking out fortunes for plastic surgery. But it's not for their noses, nipples or knockers. It's for their house plants!

LUPINS

Tired of podgy primroses, lumpy lupins and sagging sunflowers, the potty potted plant owners will pay up to $800 for a leaf tuck, $1400 for a petal lift and anything up to $3000 for a stalk enlargement.

A houseplant

Plant surgeon Dr Conrad Pissenphlaps says that an attractive plant will grow taller, produce bigger leaves and smell nicer, because it is happy with its own self-image. And Californians are queuing up at his Beverly Hills Plant Surgery. **GAY**

Stars like Oprah Winfrey, Johnny Carson, Cheers bar gay revelation Three Men In a Baby actor Ted Dalton and 3 year old trillionnaire toddler McKylie Corker must wait anything up to six years, or even double that amount (i.e. twelve) for Dr Pissenphlaps to cut bits off their pampered plants with his pinking sheers.

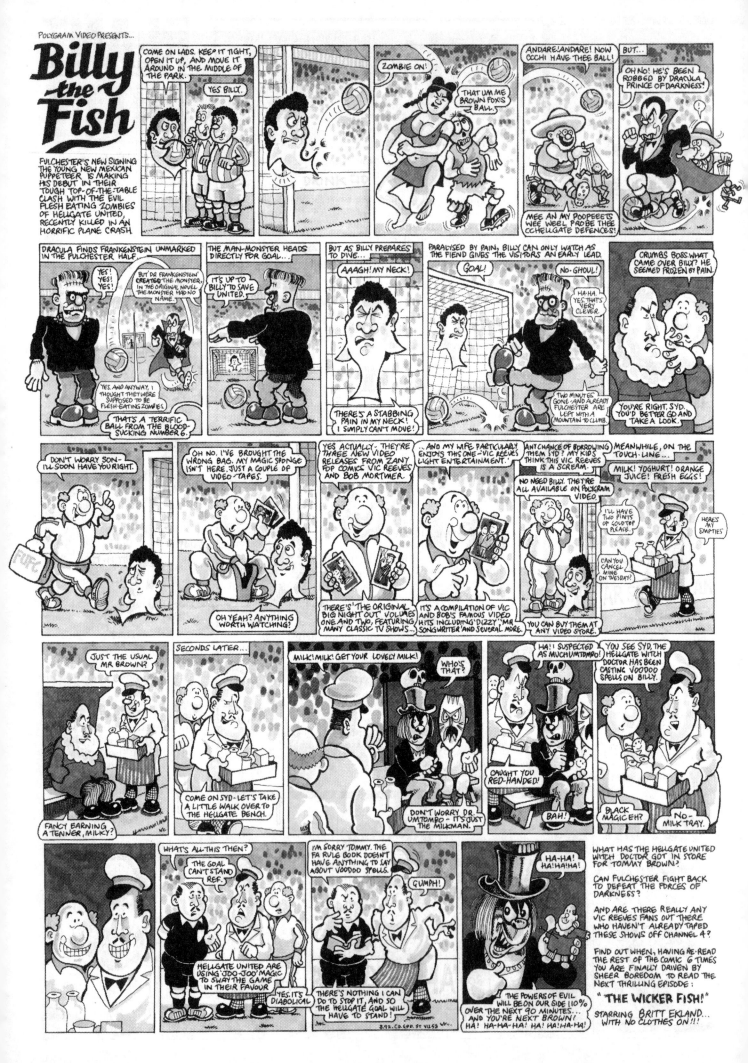

BIGGINS SAYS 'BIG UNS' ARE BEST

Flamboyant TV tubby man Christopher Biggins says that 'big is best'.

In an interview with women's magazine Jam Rag Monthly, Biggins, 41, predicts that big things are set to overtake small things in the popularity stakes.

EVEREST

And according to the outspoken star's predictions for the nineties **IN** will be big things like Mount Everest, double decker buses and elephants.

Meanwhile **OUT** will go mice, paper clips, sugar lumps, diary pencils and peas.

C.R. SMITH

In the interview Biggins admits to having a soft spot for big things, dating back to early childhood. "I used to like big things when I was a small child", he is reported as saying.

BUDGET WINDOWS

A spokesman for Harrods today confirmed Biggins' theory. "Bigger things are selling particularly well at the moment", we were told. "In fact we've already taken £2,500 this morning on sales of big things, like sofas", the spokesman reported.

D.P.C.

Meanwhile, a button shop in London's Covent Garden reported trade at a standstill. "We haven't sold a button for a fortnight", the manager told us.

Biggins - big

SPOT THE BEARD

Pictured on the right is a well known star from the world of stage and screen. But if you look carefully you'll notice that **we've given her a beard.**

We're offering a years supply of Bic razors to the first reader who correctly identifies our mystery star, and also the original owner of her beard. Send your entries on

It will probably come as no surprise to you to learn that nobody won this competition. In fact nobody entered. Anyway, if you want to know the answer, turn to page 125.

Looks familiar?

PLUM CRAZY

The latest fad from crazy California is a dating agency with a difference.

The owners of love-lorn lemons and lonely lychees are queuing up to pair off their pears, couple up their kumquats and find partners for their peaches.

FRUITS

"Research has showed that sugar levels increase and fruit tastes nicer when it is involved in a fulfilling physical relationship with other fruit". So says Dr Tschizi Bellend, Consultant Botanical Psychologist at the University College of Los Angeles' Department of Intervegetative Relationships.

FOUNDER

Dr Bellend, founder of the exclusive Beverly Hills Lonely Fruits Club now charges up to $40,000 per piece of fruit for introductions.

Is he taking the pith? Not according to former Tomorrow's World presenter Michael Rodd. Michael, speaking from his plum farm in North Wales, told us that plums kept together in a box taste quite nice, especially with custard.

HILL'S TREET BLUES

Prominent chinned TV football analyst Jimmy Hill has been down in the mouth lately, due to a shortage of his favourite sweets.

Football's Mr Know-it-all got the blues when sweet manufacturers Rowntree Mackintosh pulled the plug on his favourite nibbles.

TREETS

Jimmy's top sweet treat was 'Treets', chocolate covered peanuts with a crispy shell, sold in bright yellow packets.

But 'Treets' disappeared from sweet shop shelves in the mid-eighties during a confectionery shake-up and can no longer be bought anywhere in Britain.

Hill, 57, stockpiled packets of his favourite sweets at his West London home, buying up supplies from sweet shops all over the country. But after several years of munching, Jimmy's secret supply has run dry and the controversial commentator has been suffering withdrawal symptoms.

"Jimmy is inconsolable. Without a packet of 'Treets' in his pocket he just goes potty", one TV insider told us. "He's tried eating 'M & Ms', the brand which replaced 'Treets', but he doesn't like them", our informant revealed.

"They taste very similar, but they're all different colours and they've got 'M & M' written on the side", Hill is reported to have told colleagues.

FAVOURITE

Since running out of 'Treets' shortly after Christmas, Hill has spent most of his time locked in his bedroom, or barricaded inside his dressing room at the Match of the Day studios, refusing to come out during football matches.

"He only ever comes out at half time to pass comment

on the game", one Match of the Day colleague told us. "We're very worried about him". BBC chiefs fear Hill could follow in the footsteps of another famous sports reporter Kenneth Wolstenholme. The celebrated '66 World Cup Final commentator gave up football commentary altogether after his favourite breakfast cereal 'Klondike Pete's Golden Nuggets' were discontinued in the early seventies.

MP's SEEK SEX RULE REVIEW

Urgent reforms in Britain's sex laws are being sought by MPs fed up with constant slurs and allegations of sex scandal and impropriety involving politicians.

And among new measures they propose are:

- **EXCLUSION** for all MPs from the strict laws regarding prostitution.

- **RELAXING** of the rules regarding indecent exposure

- and **LIFTING** of the present ban on MPs carrying out acts of gross indecency.

VICTIMS

For years MPs have been the victims of countless allegations of sexual corruption. And many live in constant fear of media harassment, arrest and even imprisonment.

EXPOSED

"Having their sexual misconduct exposed can cause embarrassment and distress to an MP, and in certain cases can seriously affect their career prospects", one Commons insider told us. So now a growing number of MPs feel that strict laws governing sexual conduct should be relaxed for MPs, allowing them to endulge in acts of gross indecency, homosexuality with small boys and kinky sex including bondage, without fear of police or press reprisals.

"MPs have a uniquely difficult and stressful job to perform", we were told. "The pressures of work bring about a need for unusual, bizarre and often illegal forms of sexual relief, especially among Tories. Often kinky sex is the only relaxation available to a busy back bencher."

BIZARRE

"The existing laws regarding sexual behaviour are all well and good for the man in the street, but MPs should be exempt from these laws. I believe we are a special case", the spokesman continued.

LAVATORIES

MPs are also lobbying for better facilities at Westminster, including public lavatories on grassy lawns surrounding the Commons where MPs can meet homosexuals for the purpose of carrying out indecent acts, and regular visits to Westminster by schoolchildren and boy scout groups, to enable politicians to meet young boys.

ANN'S ADVICE ON CARPENTRY

HRH Princess Ann has spoken out strongly on the issue of carpentry.

The Princess Royal, speaking at an annual dinner of the National Society for the Protection of Certain Types of Fish of which she is Honorary President, said over a period of many years traditional forms of carpentry have almost become extinct.

JOINTS

"I find it sad that traditional close fitting hand-made joints, such as the dovetail, are rarely used by carpenters and furniture manufacturers nowadays", the Princess told the audience of over 800 fish enthusiasts.

SPLIFFS

"There was time, not so long ago, when joints between two pieces of wood were made to fit so tightly that often glue was not required", the Princess added. And she blamed modern working practices for a fall in standards throughout the carpentry trade.

Princess Ann's remarks came in the week in which she announced the launch of a new charitable foundation, The Princess Royal's Trust for the Furthering of Traditional Old Fashioned Woodwork Skills. And stars have already rallied round, promising a gala fund-raising concert to support the cause.

FOUNDATIONS

Top entertainers, among them Phil Collins, Billy Connolly plus a host of Royal sycophants have volunteered

Ann - advice

their services for the event which is expected to lose money hand over fist.

CANNON BLASTS QUEEN!

American TV cops of the seventies have launched a blistering attack on the British Monarchy.

Former top TV detectives, among them Cannon star William Conrad, have **BLASTED** the Royals, accusing them of being overpaid, out-dated and out of touch.

DINOSAUR

"The British Monarchy is an outdated institution. It's a modern-day dinosaur, and sooner or later it's going to become extinct", said the gravel voiced 22 stone actor who played porky private eye Frank Cannon in the hit series.

DO DO

His views were echoed by Jack Lord, better known to millions of seventies TV viewers as Steve McGarrett, crime fighting star of Hawaii Five O. Lord lashed out at the luxury lifestyles enjoyed by the Royals.
"It's not right that the Royals should live in luxurious palaces while everyone else in Britain is homeless", he told us.

KNUCKLE HEAD

"A right Royal rip-off". That's how bandy-legged actor Paul Michael Glaser described Britain's system of constitutional control. "The very least they could do is pay tax", continued the dynamic cardigan clad star of Starsky and Hutch. Paul's partner in crime fighting, alias actor David Hutch, agreed with his former cop colleague. "There's no doubt that the Royals perform a useful function, but their pay is out of all proportion to the amount of work they do", chipped in the actor and former singing star who's hits included 'Silver Lady'.

Soul - 'Silver Lady'

Screen cripple Ironside, who struggled against disability to bring law and order to the streets of San Fransisco, believes the Royals should hand over their cash to the poor. "They should use their millions to build hospitals, orphanages and housing for the poor", said able-bodied actor Raymond Burr.

MY LIFE BY JEFFREY BARNYARD

God, my life is boring these days. I went to the dentist on Tuesday, and he told me I'd got an abscess. He's offered to drain it for me, but I don't know. I think I'll just grin and bear it for a bit, and hope it goes away.
I might nip to the shops this afternoon. I want to buy some tinned peaches. But there's an old dragon works in the corner shop, and I loathe and detest her. So I don't think I'll bother. Looks like Ryvita for tea again. How I loath and detest the stuff.
Funny how all your friends start dying as you get older. There'll only be me left soon.
It's Brookside tonight. How I loath and detest that awful programme.
My TV's on the blink again. A man who came to repair it told me it would cost £50 to put it right. I don't think I'll bother.
I'm afraid I seem to have developed another lump behind my ear. The second one in as many months. It doesn't cause me discomfort, but I may as well have it lanced anyway.
I must have had a good drink last night. I feel bloody awful today. I fell asleep in a chair at the club last night. I'm afraid I pissed myself as usual. I've now developed something of a rash between my legs as a result. And I remain convinced that there is a swelling in my right testicle, although the doctor insists there is not. How I loath and detest doctors.
Damn that woman. I *will* have the peaches.

Cannon - blast!

But the comments of the former US TV cops last night provoked an angry response from the British TV bobbies of the seventies, who swiftly jumped to the defence of the Royals. And they criticised the American TV tecs for meddling.
"What the hell do a bunch of American actors know about our Royal Family", fumed James Ellis, alias Sergeant Burt Lynch in the long-running Z-Cars series.

ODD BALL

Burt's former TV Z-Cars colleague and subsequent Softly Softly Task Force star Frank Windsor agreed. "The Royals do a marvellous job, but their dignity prevents them from responding to attacks like these. Former American TV policemen would do well to mind their own business. They've got enough problems of their own in America".

ODD JOB

Tough guy actor Dennis Waterman, alias burly Detective Constable Jimmy Carter in TV's The Sweeney, was unavailable for comment last night. But his agent told us that Waterman, former sidekick of one-time Sweeney star TV's Inspector Morse, John Thaw, was a fan of the Royals, and he would back the British TV police in the row over Royalty.

Carter's Sweeney sidekick - Morse star Thaw

Meanwhile washboard playing comedy actor Derek Guyler, who regularly turned up as P.C. Corky in the hit series Sykes, stood up for the Queen Mother. "She does a marvellous job, God bless her. I'd like to see an American TV cop, for example David Jansen, star of Harry O, do her job."
A spokesman for Jansen, the silver-haired seventies sleuth, last night told us he was dead, and had been for some time.
We tried to speak to British actor Jack Warner, star of the ever popular Dixon of Dock Green, but we were told that he was dead as well.

LET'S HAVE A VOTE

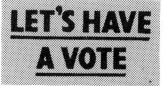

Do you agree with the American TV cops of the seventies and think that it's time Britain got rid of the Royals? Or do you back the British screen bobbies and support the Royal Family?

0898

We're having a national telephone vote to decide who's right. But unfortunately we haven't got an 0898 phone number. So we want you to write to Viz 0898 Telephone Vote Line, P.O. Box 1PT, Newcastle upon Tyne, NE99 1PT. If you post your letter at peak times please enclose 45p, or 36p at all other times. Don't worry, half of the money will be sent to British Telecom.

ELTON AND THE GENERAL PURPOSE BUILDER

WORLD EXCLUSIVE

A man who has been seen working at the home of millionaire pop star Elton John is a self employed general purpose builder, we can exclusively reveal.

Steve Fairbrother, a stocky 32-year-old, runs his business from a small yard in Guildford, Surrey, not far from Elton's £2.5 million mansion.

YELLOW PAGES

Elton, 44, met Steve after reading an ad in the Yellow Pages. In it Steve described himself as 'Prompt, friendly and reliable'. 'No job too big or too small' the ad continued. It also boasted 'Free Estimates'.

THOMSON LOCAL

Steve has been a regular visitor to the pop millionaire's lavish £6 million luxury home, often seen coming and going in his £4,500 red Escort van – believed to have been paid for using the profits from his building work, some of which has come from Elton.

BONES

The singer, 46, who often wears hats, makes no bones about his relationship with the handy man. "It's true, I've employed him to do some plastering, to build a fireplace and tile the bathroom. He's a reliable tradesman, and his prices are competitive", he confided to friends recently. And people

close to the billionaire singer say that Elton is 'delighted' with the work that has been done.

In the past few months Fairbrother is believed to have:
● **PLUMBED** in a sink in Elton's lavish £80,000 utility room.
● **REPOINTED** a chimney stack above the south facing gable of the star's £12 million farmhouse.
● **BUILT** a small retaining wall around flowerbeds outside the star's lavish £40,000 kitchen window.

SCOTTY

Neighbours living close to the multi-billionaire's £14 million hideaway describe Fairbrother as 'quiet'. "He regularly comes and goes bringing plaster, lengths of wood and tools. Sometimes he has a ladder on the top of his van", one neighbour told us.

UHURU

When we rang Tewson's Builders Supplies of Guildford, a spokesman confirmed that Fairbrother had an account with them, and revealed he had collected several lengths of dressed timber from them only last week.

Elton - paid Steve (above) for home improvements

"He ordered them on the Monday, and said he wanted them on Wednesday", we were told. Unfortunately the spokesman could not confirm that this wood was for work on Elton's mansion. "I don't know what it was for", he told us.

WIFE

When we rang Fairbrother's home – a small flat which he shares with his wife – he wasn't in. His wife Shirley, a pretty 24-year-old, offered to take a message. "My husband's out on a job at the moment", she said. "But if you give me your number I cane get him to ring you back when he comes in. Probably after six", she added.

DIVORCE

Elton, who's short-lived marriage to Brazilian beauty Renata Blauel ended in divorce, has admitted to friends that he is concerned about hair loss on the top of his head.

17

18

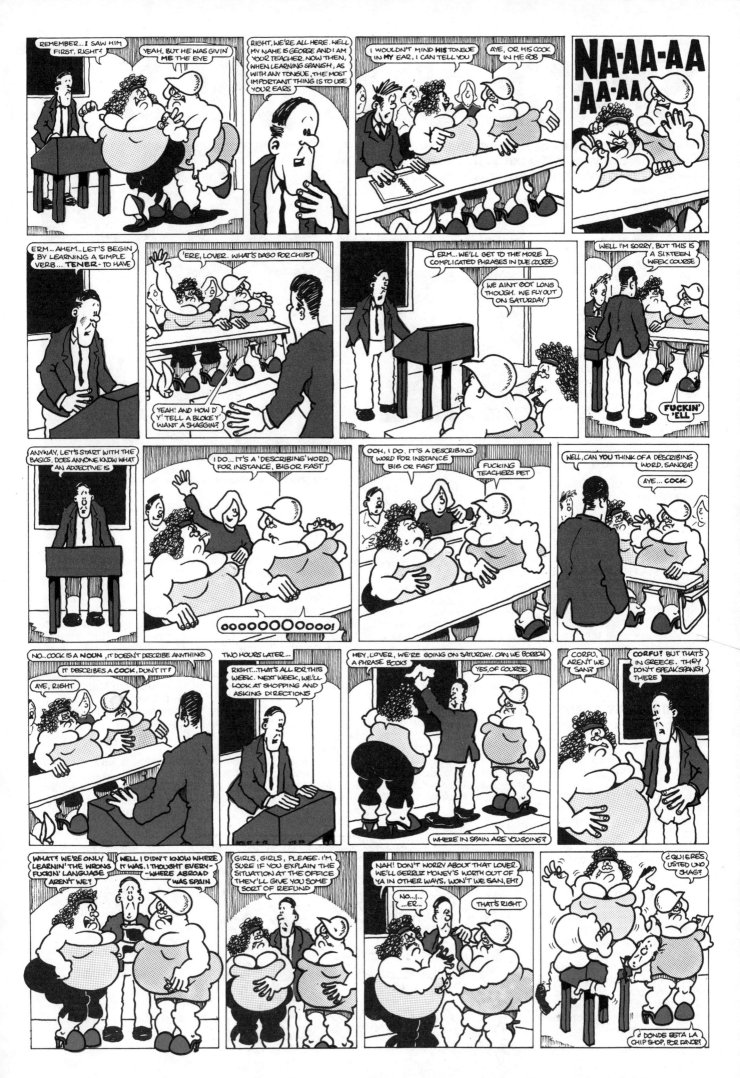

19

SPACE OLYMPICS FO

Manchester's hopes of hosting the Olympic Games in the year 2000 could be dashed if a surprise new contender enters the running.

For according to the bookies the red hot favourite to host the games isn't Manchester, Munich or Mozambique. It's Mars! For in the year 2000 we may be witnessing the first ever *Olympic Games in space.*

By our Science Correspondent Dr. Stanley Jordan

Moore - life on Mars

MARS

Leading 'astrologers', or space scientists, among them Patrick Moore, have long believed that there is life on Mars. And if a parallel life form has developed on the surface of the red planet, it is almost certain that they will have developed a form of 'Olympic Games' similar to our own.

MARATHON

And among Martian athletes the most popular events will probably be:

* **TARGET SHOOTING** using lazer guns firing at targets in another universe.

* **CYCLING** on jet powered mono-cycles. In the 'Rouge Prix de Mars', the Martian equivalent of the Tour de France, three legged cyclists regularly travel at ten times the speed of sound.

* **FENCING** with bright shiny sonic sword beams (like the ones on Star Wars).

* **THREE DAY EVENT-ING** on giant, poisonous equine space lizards, 30 feet long.

TOPIC

In the first ever inter-galactic Olympics competitors from Earth will be at a disadvantage in many sports. However, certain space factors could dramatically improve our performance in others.

BOUNTY

For example, *weightlessness* will lead to spectacular performances in the high jump, pole vault and shot putting events. Indeed, rescue space shuttles will have to hover in the atmosphere above the Olympic Stadium to save any pole vaulters who accidentally vault into space.

The planet Mars has no grass or water. So field sports will take place on bright red Martian astro-turf, the surface of which is hot enough to toast muffins, or piklets (a sort of flat, Martian crumpet). And the lack of water will mean that all the swimming events will have to take place in other liquids, such as white spirit or vinegar. British swimmers Adrian Moorhouse and Duncan Goodhew are already rumoured to be training in turps.

CUTTY SARK

There is no sunlight on Mars – Martian athletes see using special infra-red vision. However, terrestrial competitors will overcome this problem by wearing 'miners' style helmets complete with plutonium powered headlamps.

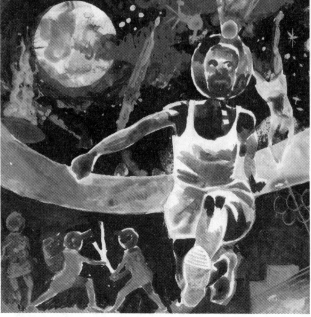

The date: 2000, The venue: Mars. Is this the Olympics of the future?

Sports clothing manufacturers are already working flat out to produce shirts, shorts and socks suitable to withstand the rigors of the space atmosphere. Conventional kits and footwear would simply implode in the space vacuum on Mars. Adidas are thought to be leading the field, having gone into partnership with cooking foil giants Alcan to produce the world's first heat resistant tin foil plated teflon soled sports shoe, the 'Adidas Apollo'. But the bad news for parents is that the new shoe, set to become the height of teenage fashion, does not come cheap. Enormous research and development costs will lead to a likely price tag of around £12 million 99p a pair.

Communications and transport to the games could be a problem due to the enormous distances involved. 'Live' TV coverage of events in the Olympic Stadium will actually take 4 months to reach our TV screens. And because of the sheer distance involved, athletes hoping to compete in the Martian Olympiad will have to leave early. Next week in fact. For a journey by conventional space travel to Mars currently takes up to 8 years to complete, depending on 'orbits'.

VICTORY

For unlike towns and countries, planets move about, and sometimes when you get there they've gone. So you have to start looking for them again.

BEAGLE

But the good news for British athletes such as Joanne Conway and Wilf O'Reilly is that the lack of gravity on Mars means that everything happens in slow motion, so they won't hurt themselves when they fall on their arses.

ALSATION

Security at the first Martian Olympics will be at record levels. Indeed it will have to be. For the Martians are a

THINGS AINT WHAT THEY USED TO BE

R THE YEAR 2000! ⬡⬡⬡

Britain's athletes ready to get set to prepare for the Olympics on Mars

war-like race who, like Germany, do not take kindly to losing. And just as Germany's defeat in the 1936 Munich Olympics lead to the Second World War, so an Earth victory on Mars could lead to a full scale invasion of our planet by Martian battle rockets and 'Red Warrior' flying saucers.

LABRADOR

As usual, it'll be up to Britain to defend the Earth single handed. However, an impressive arsenal of space weaponry already under development would soon put paid to the alien invasion.

FISHER

Britain's space weaponry in the year 2000 will include:

* Hawker Hyper-Drive nuclear space fighter rockets with 360 degree space guided lazer missiles, and big machine guns.

* The Saturn 4 Earth-to-space missile, capable of taking out a whole fleet of Martian space rockets every half second.

* The Mohican Strike Delta Space Helicopter carrying a special top secret 'seek and destroy' robot guided anti-planetary nuclear obliteration device code-named 'Battlemaster'.

* The Jupiter Bomb - the most powerful weapon known to man, and capable of blowing up the entire universe – ten times over. Every second – for *ten minutes*.

CROMETY

In a high tec space age 'Blitz' scenario the Cockney spirit will once again be tested to the full as Martian 'Death Rain' rockets pour down onto London while the population huddles together in tube stations, singing along to the sound of Dame Sinead O'Connor, the darling of the forces in the year 2000.

TYNE

Alas, the Queen Mum won't be much good this time round. For at the ripe old age of 100, Britain's favourite great great great granny will be confined to a Royal bathchair, and will probably be gibbering away like a fool in the corner of some remote Royal garden.

Britain's athletes yesterday welcomed news of the Mars Olympics, and declared "We're raring to go!".

Long distance runner **Brendan Foster** was full of optimism. "It will certainly make a novel change competing on another planet. It's a great challenge for me, and I only hope that I'll be a suitable ambassador for my planet".

SEVERN

Strong-man panto ex-cop shot putter **Geoff Capes** was apprehensive about journeying to Mars. "I'd relish the challenge of competing against space aliens, but it would be a long way to travel. Sixteen years is a long time to be away from your wife and kids", said 'gentle giant' Geoff.

THAMES

Wily fox Canadian snooker hearthrob **Cliff Thorburn** was intrigued. "Owing to weightlessness there would be an intrinsic problem in keeping the balls on the table", Cliff pointed out. "Perhaps snooker could be played on a three dimensional basis, in a cube perhaps, with a pocket on each corner. Or a conventional table could be placed within a drum spinning on an axis to create an artificial or 'centrepedal' form of gravity", added Cliff.

T.V. AM

Cliff's Cockney colleague, whirlwind **Jimmy White**, had his own suggestion. "The game could be played inside a huge centrifuge, with two tables place diametrically opposite each other, spinning at a constant speed of, say, 200 r.p.m., thus simulating the effects of the Earth's gravity. Mind you, players would soon become nausious, and vomit. And besides, snooker isn't in the Olympics", pointed out whizz kid White.

Brendan Foster yesterday

British boxing champ **Lloyd Hunnigan** was sceptical about the whole idea of a Mars Olympics. "I challenge the basic hypothesis of intelligent life on Mars", stormed the champ. "Because of high radiation levels, any life on Mars would have to be silicon based rather than carbon based like ourselves. And in order to survive, Martian life forms would need to have allumina silicate shells to protect their DNA from mutagenesis. It is therefore highly improbable that they would have developed beyond a simple algi or diaton life form", Lloyd told us yesterday.

COMPACTA

Bad news for British athletes is that winners will NOT be in line to collect gold, silver or bronze medals for their efforts. These metals are commonplace on Mars, and would be thought of by Martians as nothing special. Instead Martian medal winners collect trophies made out of Mars' most coverted materials – coal, soil and plywood.

Charity Fish book launched

Prince would like to be a cod. And Edwina Currie would like to be a dab.

These are just some of the celebrities who have contributed to the book 'I Wish I Was A Fish'.

BRAINCHILD

The book is the brainchild of seventies keyboard wizard Rick Wakeman, and all the proceeds will go to charity. Complete with illustrations by pint-sized Aussie songstress Danni Minogue and featuring a painting of a haddock by The Bachelors on the cover, the book is published next week by Soufflé Books priced £3.99, although copies will be available in large piles from bargain book bins for 50p each two weeks later.

23

WE TURN THE TABL

SHOW HOSTS

On TV they look cool, intelligent and totally in control.

As they fire questions at hopeful contestants and hand out the glittering prizes, everyone know that the TV quizmasters are in charge.

BRAINY

But just how brainy are the TV game show hosts. Without the answers written down in front of them how many questions would **THEY** get right if the spotlight was on them? We decided to turn the tables and test the intelligence of these telly gents by quizzing the quizmasters at their own game.

KRYPTON

On screen Krypton Factor host Gordon Burn looks suave, sophisticated and super-intelligent. But when we rang Burn at 7.30 in the morning he sounding anything but bright. "What do you want? You've got me out of bed", he croaked.

STARTER

As a starter for ten we asked gameshow Gordon what was the capital city of Peru? Struggling to answer our easy starter Burn asked us to repeat the question. We did, but he was obviously stumped. For gormless Gordon simply hung up the phone.

MAIN COURSE

Our next contestant was Bob Monkhouse, host of a hatfull of shows. From the Golden Shot to Celebrity Squares, Bob has a Full House of quiz show credits to his name. But the $64,000 question is *how brainy is Bob?*

Bob - brainy?

At first he seemed reluctant to take part in our quiz. As we explained the rules he constantly interrupted, telling us to speak to his agent. But he soon regained his composure.

PUDDING

"Alright, alright. What's this question then?" snapped Bob. "What B describes a person who speaks fluently in two languages?" we asked.
"That's easy', replied Bob. "Bilingual".

COFFEE

Although Bob's answer was correct, we couldn't give him a point. "Sorry Bob, we have to accept the *first* word you say", we explained. "And as you said "That's easy' first, strictly speaking you got the answer wrong." "That's ridiculous", fumed Bob, before hanging up the phone.
They don't mind dishing out the petty rules and regulations, but it's a different story when the TV game show hosts are on the receiving end.

POKED

Tubby comic Les Dawson has poked fun at hundreds of guests on the popular TV game show Blankety Blank. But how would he feel of the jokes were on him?

HOLIDAY RETREAT

Deadpan Dawson sounded surprised when we rang him at his Corfu holiday retreat and offered him six catagories of question to choose from. "Where did you get this number from?" he snapped. Les was less then co-operative, so we chose a catagory for him, and selected a question on science.

Les - holiday home

We asked Dawson which metal has the chemical symbol 'Ag'? There was a long silence, before Les repeated his enquiry. "Who gave you this number?"

HOLIDAY HOME

We explained that the tables were turned, and that today *we* would be asking the questions, pointing out that he had only 4 seconds left in which to answer. Les's reply was unprintable.

HOT SEAT

Next we decided to put Gambit presenter Fred Dinenage in the hot seat and managed to track him down to an office at London Weekend Television.
"Your name please", we asked the 52-year-old presenter.
"It's Fred here. Who's that?" he replied.

HOT BED

"Mr. Dinenage, you have two minutes to answer questions on the life and work of Charles Darwin starting from... *now. On which island group did Darwin make his study of finches the result of which formed the basis for his theory of natural selection?*"

HOT POT

"I'm sorry... who is this?" replied Fred.
"No, the Galapagos Archi-

Noel - tidy beard

pelago. Aboard which ship did Darwin set sail as Scientific Officer in Dezember 1852?"
"Look, I'm sorry, but I don't know what this is all about", said a flustered Dinenage, wasting valuable time. And by the end of his two minutes he had failed to score a single point.

TOP MAN

When we rang Telly Addicts top ·man Noel Edmonds he displayed a remarkable lack of TV knowledge. House Party host Noel was busy recording his shown when we called.
"I'm sorry, can I get Noel to call you back", the receptionist asked us. We decided to leave Noel a simple question about Thunderbirds, and asked if he'd get back to us with the answer. A week later we still hadn't heard from Mr. Edmonds. He's obviously not a *telly addict* after all.

TOP CAT

Of all the quizmasters and game show hosts we rang, not *one* made it into the second round of our quiz. Derek Batey was among the few who managed to score a point, correctly saying that his wife would keep the oven gloves on a hook in the pantry.
So there were no takers for our star prize – a brand new Ford Fiesta and a matching luggage set.

ES ON THE T.V. GAME

CAN YOU DO ANY BETTER?

Here's a chance to pit your wits against the TV quizmasters. Listed below are some of the questions we asked the quiz show kings along with the answers they gave. Fill in your own answers in the blank column on the right. (The correct answers are listed below).

You have thirty seconds to answer these questions starting from *now!*

	BOB HOLNESS	JIM BOWEN	BAMBER GASGOINE	Your name ....
1. GEOGRAPHY What is the capital city of France?	*"Erm … is it Dunkirk?"*	*"Paris"*	*"I think it's Spain"*	
2. POP MUSIC Name one member of hit sixties group The Beatles.	*"Ringo Starr"*	*"Paul McCartney"*	*"Oh, I don't know. Cliff Richard?"*	
3. HISTORY In what year did the Battle of Hastings take place?	*"1942 … no … 1943"*	*"Around about 1812 wasn't it?"*	*"The battle of what? I've never heard of it."*	
4. SCIENCE Who invented gravity whilst playing with apples?	*"Science … that must be Einstien"*	*"That's easy, Robert Louis Stephenson"*	*"Oh dear. I'm not doing very well, am I?"*	
5. GENERAL KNOWLEDGE Which Gulf War general was nicknamed 'Stormin' Norman'?	*"Norman Wisdom?"*	*"Norman Vaughan?"*	*"Don't tell me … erm … it's on the tip of my tongue. Norman.. Norman … **Norman Conquest**"*	

How did you do? Here are the correct answers: 1. Paris. 2. John Lennon. 3. 1066. 4. Isaac Walton. 5. General Norman Swortchcough.

CHEATS!

That's how one TV insider described Britain's TV game show hosts.

And he claimed that the majority of TV quizmasters don't know the answers to the questions they ask – *they look them up in books!*

And we were told that TV's quiz show king, mega-brainy Mastermind Magnus Magnusson is in fact – *a dunce.*

DUNCE

"He's just showing off when he asks all his big, clever questions. Little do the audience know, he doesn't even think the questions up, never mind know the answers", said our insider.

INDEPENDENT

A spokesman for Mastermind confirmed that independent question setters write questions for the show. When we rang Magnusson's Iceland home his wife told us he wasn't in. "Magnus is very upset about this whole business. He doesn't want to talk to anyone", claimed the fraudster's wife.

GUARDIAN

We then rang Leslie Crowther's former school to find out whether the bespectacled 'Sale of the Century' star had got any 'O' levels. But a spokesman told us that files

Crowther - missing files

on Crowther which contained his exam results had mysteriously gone 'missing'.

25

29

LETTERBOX

It all `ads` up to a sell out

LetterBocks
Viz Commick
P.O. Box 1 PT
Newcasle upon Tyne
NE99 1PT

I'm fed up with Viz's blatent 'selling out' to advertising. Once again I open up my favourite comic to see Billy the Fish being used to promote some stupid records or video company. Can't you keep this crap off the pages? The last issue was so bad I had to go down to 'Mitch's Cafe' in Emmerich, here in sunny Germany, where you can find real German beer and as much fresh schnitzel as you can eat, and all for the price of twenty tabs. Mmmmmmitchs! For the real taste of Germany.

Mitch B
Mitch's Cafe
Wohnung 1
Gerhard Storm Str. 7
4240 Emmerich
Germany

Last night my teenage son arrived home from school early and caught me parading in front of our bedroom mirror wearing high heels, ladies' underwear, a dress and make-up. I almost died of embarrassment – until I remembered, I'm his mother.
Do I win £5?

Mrs T. Tank-Engine
Sodor

Direction information request

Can any of your readers tell me the best route by car from Northampton to Reading and the approximate journey time, as I have a job interview there tomorrow. Any help much appreciated.

R. Murray
Northampton

Dear Jim, Please fix it for me to go on a guided tour of a pornographic film production company's studios.

N. Neo
Bristol

In response to your recent request for pictures of people sticking their heads out of washing machines, I have a story which might interest you. I was stirring soup in the kitchen recently when suddenly my next door neighbour appeared out of the cooker, playing the harmonica. Luckily my wife was on hand with the camera to photograph the scene.

Stanley Spence
Belfast

This is the final call for readers who have photographs of people with musical instruments sticking their head out of white kitchen goods. Send your pictures to our usual Letterbocks address. There's a microwave oven and a trumpet to the sender of the best picture we receive.

People often say 'Early to bed, early to rise – makes a man healthy, wealthy and wise'. Try telling my dad that. For the last 40 years he's gone to bed at 8pm and got up at 5am. He's dying of cancer, flat broke and as thick as shit.

Mr Lights
Dollar

In response for your request for readers to write if they live in a place with a girl's name, my youngest daughter – Welwyn Garden City – has a friend who lives in the town of the same name. Do I get a tenner?

P. Morton
Southampton

Poetry problem

My name is Robert Burns and I am unable to write any poetry. I wonder if there are any other readers who are unable to live up to their famous namesakes?

Robert Burns
Paisley

Robert Burns of Paisley (Letterbox, this issue) is not alone. May name is Isambard Kingdom Brunel, but I couldn't build a bridge to save my fucking life. In fact I tried to build a barbecue in our back yard last summer and it fell over.

Isambard Kingdom Brunel
Arbroath

The problem with public transport is not the availability, frequency or efficiency of services provided, it is the fact that people who use it smell.

M. Thigh
Cambridge

Time called on costly carrot tops

I have watched with interest the debate on ginger haired people unfolding on you Letterbocks page. I am a hairdresser, and have been for nearly forty years. However this year I have finally had to ban ginger people from coming into my shop. Over the years they have blunted scissors and broken combs with their coarse wiry hair. They have even made my razor go rusty with their prickly, orange stubble. I have nothing personal against these people, but enough is enough.

Percy Green
Skemersdale

Some people say that swearing is the sign of a limited vocabulary. Well, I write dictionaries for a living and have a big vocabulary, but I still swear.
So that fucks that theory, doesn't it?

Lornal Knight
Editor
Collins English Dictionaries
Glasgow

Delia Smith told viewers there is nothing worse than a soggy souffle. As an AIDS sufferer I have to disagree with Miss Smith's somewhat selfish view.

D.R
Kent

I wonder if any of your readers would like to marry me? I'm a tidy bit with big tits who likes cooking and doesn't mind pushing the Hoover round a bit.

R. Bint
Llanelli

Essex man throws down the gauntlet

I live in Braintree, Essex. Can any of your readers beat that?

Barry Lamb
Braintree, Essex

Come on readers. Where do YOU live? There's ten pounds for the best letter we receive, and two microwave ovens for the first person who lives in Ipswich.

I was recently very worried when a group of burly youths clambered aboard my bus carrying baseball bats. Then I remembered – I am the team manager for the New York Yankees.

F. Nosejob
New York

We defeated the French at Agincourt and Waterloo. We beat them at football and rugby. We've bailed them out of two world wars which they foolishly started but couldn't finish. And what do they do? They set fire to our sheep.
Some people are just bad loosers.

H. Helicopter
Luton

TopTips

CONVINCE neighbours that you own a racing cat by draping a small cloth over its back, putting binoculars round your neck, and leading it around your lawn.

Mrs Wm. Holland
Stanton-in-Leak
Derbyshire

DON'T buy gift vouchers for your children and friends this Christmas. You'll find that bank notes are available in a wide range of colours and sizes and they are accepted by all high street shops.

C. McKeown
Fleetwood, Lancs

STICK pictures of a favourite film actress over Fergie's head on any Royal pictures or souvenirs you have around the house. I now have an attractive portrait of Prince Andrew with Hollywood stunner Michelle Pfeiffer on my mantle piece.

Mrs Dawn Potts
Cheltenham

CONVINCE friends that you have a high powered job in the City by leaving for work at 6 am every morning, arriving home at 10 at night, never keeping social appointments and dropping down dead at the age of 36.

S. James
Barnes

FOIL fiddling taxi drivers by taking polaroid photographs of street signs as you pass them. At the end of your journey you can confront him with evidence if he has taken an unnecessarily long route.

R. Holmes
Putney

GIRLS. Practice being an air hostess by standing up at the end of the aisle and demonstrating emergency landing procedures every time you get on a bus.

Mrs Joyce Clooney
Littlehampton

BEAT police speed traps by stopping your car every 200 yards and pretending to mess around under the bonnet. This way traffic cops will be unable to accurately record your speed for any length of time.

S. Daniels
Halifax

DEPLETE the world's forests by writing third rate paperback thrillers on environmental issues which become best sellers and require tons of wood pulp to produce.

Bob Smith
Fulchester

OH YEAH? And what the fuck is Viz made out of then?

B. Elton
South Kensington

BUS DRIVERS. Pretend you're an airline pilot by wedging your accelerator pedal down with a heavy book, securing the steering wheel with some old rope, and then strolling back along your bus chatting casually to the passengers.

Mrs Joyce Clooney
Littlehampton

SHORTER, thinner lengths of wire connecting appliances to the mains will probably reduce the amount of electricity that they use.

Peter Redman
Devizes

IF catching a bus, always take a polaroid photograph of the queue so that when the bus arrives any argument about people pushing in can be easily settled.

R. Holmes
Putney

WHILE queuing to buy stamps at the post office keep some loose change in your right hand pocket. As each minutes passes by, transfer one coin into your left hand pocket. When you eventually get served the number of coins in your left pocket will tell you exactly how many minutes you have been waiting.

Mr K. Walsh
Epsom

ROLL carpet slippers in breadcrumbs, bake until golden brown, then tell friends you are wearing Findus Crispy Pancakes.

H. Lloyd
Runcorn

FAST food restaurant staff. Fill cups full of ice before pouring soft drinks so that customers get only a fraction of what they pay for.

B. King
London

Send us YOUR inovative, imaginative or energy saving ideas. There's a crisp tenner for every one we publish (starting in the next issue). Plus a microwave oven for the best one we receive. And a hat. And a box of cigars.

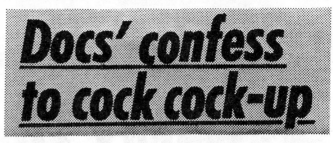

Docs' confess to cock cock-up

For many years medical experts have believed that the size of a man's penis is not important to his partner, it's what he does with it that matters.

But now red faced doctors are admitting "We got it wrong". For scientific research has shown that if you haven't got a great big cock, there's something wrong with you. And that leaves the vast majority of men with a big – or rather a **small** – problem.

BIG COCKS

People with small parts lead a miserable life. Shunned by girls, avoided by friends. They live their life in solitude, never invited to parties. Their parents are ashamed of them. They are misfits in a world where only big cocks count. But now we are offering them a change to escape from the living hell of having a small knob.

GIRTH

A company in Manchester, aided by top scientific researchers in the U.S.A., have marketed a remarkable and truly amazing PENIS ENLARGER. Looking like a baby bottle with a pipe on the end, the **Vacuum Penis Developer** can 'increase your length and girth by up to 4 inches'. And in order to publicise this monumental medical breakthrough we are giving away a DOZEN of these dick stretchers – each worth every penny of £29.99 – to the first twelve readers with small penis's who complete and send in the coupon below. The 12 prizes will be despatched under plain cover, except for the words 'Penis Enlarger' written on the parcel.

FLACID

This exclusive Viz reader offer is open to all male readers whose member, when flacid, is less than 2½ inches long. But don't worry if you don't win a free Penis Enlarger. You can expand your knob by ordering one from the 'First Choice' advertisement which appears in our Cheapskates Parade. (Orders will be sent under plain cover).

34

36

Photographs by Colin D.

THE END

At last...it's OFFICIAL!

MORRISEY IS A TWAT

Cult pop singer Morrisey — hailed as hero by his fanatical fans — is a twat, according to experts.

And that will come as bad news to his many admirers who have worshipped the pop idol since he came to fame as lead singer of The Smiths.

VIDEO

Professor Ivan Sogorski of Barrow-in-Furness University's Department of Advanced Human Behavioural Studies came to his dramatic conclusion about the star after listening to many of his records and watching video footage of his TV appearances. And he summed up his professional opinion in a few short words.

TWAT

"The man is an absolute twat", he told us.

ARSEHOLE

Professor Sogorski cited examples of behaviour which had lead him to his controversial conclusion. "Take for example Mr Morrisey's appearance on Top Of The Pops in the early eighties when he wore oversized shirts, National Health glasses, a hearing aid, and

EXCLUSIVE

flailed about the stage with daffodils sticking out of his back pocket. Clearly, even the most casual analysis could only conclude this to be the behaviour of an arsehole', said the Professor.

CRAP

As a part of his painstaking research, Professor Sogorski consulted a colleague to obtain a second independent opinion. "I submitted manuscipts and recordings of many Morrissey songs to a leading Professor of Composition at the Royal College of Music, and he says they are crap".

BULLSHIT

The Professor quoted examples of Morrisey's song titles as further evidence to support his views. "Girl In A Coma. Big Mouth Strikes Again. Heaven Knows I'm Miserable Now. These are all bullshit", said Professor Sogorski.

During his career Morrisey has endeared himself to a huge cult following of pop fans, among them many students, and has also won artistic acclaim for his work.

WANKER

But Professor Sogorski's comments are bound to fuel speculation that whilst some of his songs might be quite good, the man is, quite frankly, a bit of an arsehole. "I am convinced Morrisey is a twat, and anyone who says otherwise is a wanker", said the Professor yesterday. Professor Sogorski last hit the headlines in 1988 when he claimed that page three model Samantha Fox was a "boiler".

'Fuck' is OK

Britain's swearing chiefs are set to lift the ban on many rude words, among them 'fuck' and 'cunt'.

And the shock move will be a spanner in the works for many 'adult humour' magazines, 'alternative' comedians and Channel 4 programmes for whom rude words are vital ingredients. Indeed, the downgrading of words like 'fuck' from rude to slightly rude will leave many *blue* comics *red* faced.

BASTARD

In the past, rude works like 'shit' and 'bastard' have been downgraded, and are now in common usage, upsetting only Mary Whitehouse and few other old crocks. But the de-rudening of many remaining obscenities will leave genuine foul mouths with a limited arsenal of vulgarity from which to choose.

Swear bosses green light to blue comics

One English language expert believes that brand new expletives may have to be invented, or existing mild obscenities upgraded to replace ageing rude words. "there's a chance that words like 'kipper', 'snatch' or 'fanny' may soon be rude", he told us.

PISS FLAPS

When we asked him about 'beef curtains' he said he wasn't sure, and that he'd have to look it up.

Let's face it - you could get hit by a BUS tomorrow

go on ~ HAVE A FAG!

39

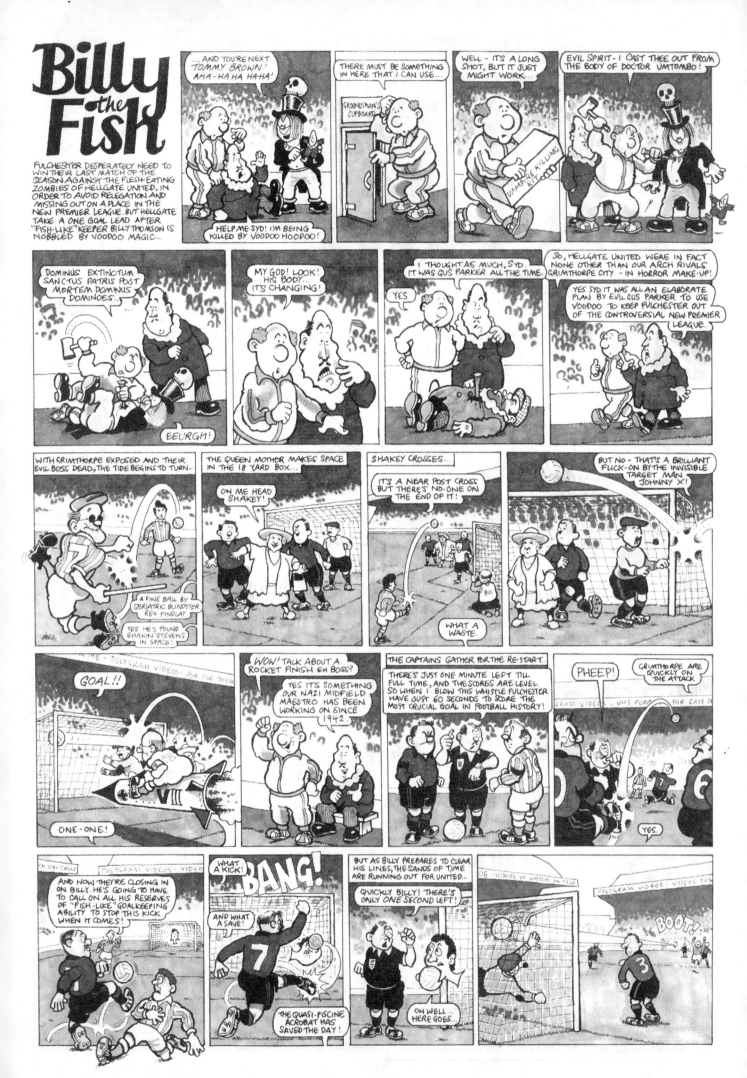

41

43

WE ask YOU to ask YOURSELVES the question
HOW PROMISCUOU THE STARS? ~ in YOUR OPINION?

Do you think they're prim and proper, or stop-outs and slags. How would YOU assess the sexual promiscuity of the stars?

Most people aren't entirely sure exactly what they think about the sexual promiscuity of TV celebrities. It may be something you haven't thought a great deal about. Or perhaps having thought about it, you still aren't entirely sure where you stand. Or if you were, maybe you've forgotten. It's easily done.

Anyway, now's your chance to find out once and for all exactly what you think about it. All you have to do is complete this survey, answering A, B or C for each question. Then tot up your total, and your final score will reveal how YOU personally perceive the imagined sexual promiscuity of the stars. You never know - it could be a real eye opener!

1. You ring up TV's Cilla Black and she accepts your offer of a 'Blind Date'. But where would she suggest you go?
(a) To the local pub for a quiet drink in the company of some other friends.
(b) To a cheerful local restaurant for a pizza and a chat.
(c) To the local 'adults only' private cinema to view a raunchy XXX rated Swedish film – from a double seat in the back row!

2. After a pleasant first date with TV's Wogan stand-in Sue Lawley you discover that you have missed the last bus home. What would Sue do?
(a) Suggest that you share a taxi, and go halfers on the fare.
(b) Walk home together chatting away in the moonlight.
(c) Kneck on with you at the bus stop for half an hour, giving you several embarrassing love bites on your neck.

3. In the queue at the record shop you notice 'perfickly' formed Darling Bud star Catherine Zeta Jones in the queue in front of you. You playfully slap her on the bottom. How would she react?
(a) She would turn round, slap you in the face, and then complain to the shop manager about your behaviour.
(b) Smile, and playfully tell you to "stop larkin' about".
(c) Wink seductively, slip her hotel room key into your pocket, and blow you a kiss as she saunters sexily out of the door.

4. You are at a night club dancing with crazy 'Miss Cathcart', actress, TV scatter-brain Sue Pollard. She's had four snakebites. Suddenly the DJ plays Chris de Burgh's Lady In Red, and

Lawlwy - love bites

Ross - mess

Sue insists on a smoochy, slow dance. How far would she let you go before the record ends? Would she:
(a) Allow your hands to slip down her back and stroke her bottom a bit.
(b) Allow you to kiss her neck and gently nibble her ear lobes.
(c) Let you give her a lingering French kiss while one hand goes in her bra and the other firmly kneads her buttocks.

5. You jump into the back of a taxi, only to find that someone else has already got in from the other side. They suggest you share the cab. To your surprise it's none other than pint sized Aussie temptress Kylie Minogue. She's had a few drinks. What do you reckon you could get in the three miles before she is due to get out of the cab?
(a) Nowt.
(b) Tops.
(c) Tops and fingers.

6. You've invited suave TV chat show host Jonathan Ross to the opera as a special birthday treat. But you soon realise he is bored. What would he do?
(a) Occasionally nod off during the performance, and apologise afterwards.
(b) Make a polite excuse and escape to the bar for the duration.
(c) Discreetly play with himself for half an hour or so and then pop to the toilet to clean up the mess.

7. You nip into your local for a drink and are surprised to find saucy Transvision Vamp singer Wendy James serving behind the bar. At closing time you offer her a lift home and she accepts. When you get to her flat what would she do?
(a) Say 'goodnight' and briskly disappear indoors.
(b) Chat for a few moments then exchange phone numbers with you before giving you a goodnight peck on the cheek.
(c) Drag you into her flat for a wild night of kinky sex handcuffed to her black leather waterbed.

8. It's your brother's stag night and you're on a pub crawl. In the twelfth pub that you enter you notice Clare Short, the vociferous Labour MP, is chatting with friends in a corner. You fancy a bit of entertainment, so the lads have a bit of a whip round and get a hundred quid in a hat. In your estimation, what form of entertainment would she be prepared to provide in return for the cash.
(a) She would sing a song for you, but only if everyone else joined in. And she would then donate the money to a worthy cause.
(b) She'd hop onto a table and perform a raunchy can-can to the drunken cheers of the crowd.
(c) Perform a lewd and suggestive strip tease culminating in an indecent simulated sex act involving your brother's nuts.

WE'VE JUST HAD THE DINING ROOM DONE IN A TANGERINE AND LIME CHECK WALLPAPER TO GO WITH THE SWIRLY PURPLE CARPET AND TURQUOISE CURTAINS. ITS REALLY NICE.

WAITER. THIS SOUP HAS NO TASTE.

ST.

S ARE

Here's how to find out

Winner - 3 times killer?

9. Imagine an unlikely scenario in which you are in bed with stunning 'Woman of Substance' actress Jenny Seagrove experimenting with an exotic selection of battery powered love toys. Suddenly in walks her Deathwish director hubby Michael Winner. What do you think he would do?

(a) Punch you in the nose and send you scurrying off with your trousers around your ankles.

(b) Shoot both you and Miss Seagrove dead, before turning the weapon on himself to complete a tragic triple love slaying.

(c) Strip off to reveal a saucy spandex play suit, complete with nipple tassles, grab the biggest love toy, turn it up to full power, and join in the fun, shouting "room for one more on top".

10. You are enjoying a Granada TV tour of the Coronation Street studios, when you take a wrong turning and end up in the stars' dressing room. The entire cast of the show are in the room in various stages of undress. What would they do?

(a) Politely ask you to leave and point you in the direction of the tour party.

(b) Offer you a cup of tea and offer to sign autographs for you.

(c) Seductively undo your trousers and lead you through into their Turkish steambath whereupon everyone strips naked and embarks upon a two-day Roman style orgy of depraved sex, during which you watch as Alex Gilroy spanks the pert buttocks of Gail Tilsley while Bett Lynch performs shaven oral pleasure on Jack Duckworth. As the temperature soars, you are invited to join in as a seven-way gang bang commences in which Mike Baldwin, Curly Watts, Eddie Yates, Mr Holdsworth, Des Barnes, Percy Sugden and Jim McDonald pull a train on Elsie Tanner.

Sharples - Roman orgy

How did you do?

Now let's see how you did.
If you answered mostly A, your opinion of the stars is that they are not particularly promiscuous. Given the choice between sex and a cup of tea, you'd probably expect them to have a cup of tea.
If you answered mostly B, then you probably think the stars are a bit more promiscuous than the people did who answered mostly A.
If you answered mostly C then you, more than anyone else, think the stars are promiscuous. And the fact that you are still reading this drivel suggests that you must be pretty bored and have nothing better to do. But thanks for your pound anyway.

EURO THREAT TO DAILY PINTA

Britain's daily doorstep deliveries of milk are set to become a thing of the past when the Channel Tunnel eventually opens for business later in the year.

For top dairy experts believe our friendly milkmen will be tempted through the tunnel to make their deliveries in other European countries.

OPENING

The opening of the first ever direct link between Britain and France will mean an overnight transport revolution for road users. Motorists will be able to pop to Paris instead of Peterborough, drive to Dunkirk instead of Dundee, motor to Marseilles instead of Manchester, or visit Versailles instead of somewhere beginning with a 'V'. And milk chiefs fear that milkmen will be lured to the continent by lucrative orders of extra yoghurt and fresh orange juice.

DOORSTEP

Up until now doorstep deliveries have been unheard of in countries like France and Germany, where the population traditionally trek to the corner shop to buy their milk, in much the same way that we buy bread, cheese and lavatory paper.

JUMP

And milk chiefs believe that lazy foreigners will jump at the opportunity to have their pintas delivered to the door. And the resulting rush of milk floats through the tunnel will leave a desperate shortage in Britain, where **MILLIONS** of pints of milk may go sour waiting weeks or even months to be delivered.

One milkman we spoke to admitted that if the money was right, he'd deliver in Europe. "Business in Britain is bad, and if the foreigners want extra milk or yoghurt, I'll be over there like a shot", he told us.

BUMPER

Ice cream vans also look set to join the Euro-drain, leaving Britain for the sunnier streets of Europe, and bumper sales of lollies, cones and soft drinks.
"The traditional sound of the ice cream van playing its tune on a sunny summer's afternoon will be lost forever unless we act now", Conservative MP Anthony Regents-Park predicted.

Part of an ice cream van yesterday

"Unless we place strict controls on the tunnel, the traffic is all going to be one way. There'll be queues of milk floats and ice cream vans miles long waiting to get to France, and all we'll get coming the other way will be a handful of old men pedalling their bicycles up the wrong side of the road and trying to sell us onions at vastly inflated prices", he added.

Time for change

I'm sick and tired of calls for proportional representation. Why move the goalposts when the rules are the same for both teams?

There's nothing wrong with our voting system. Compared to banana republics like France, we get a bloody fair deal.

But is it not the case that he who pays the piper calls the tune?

I suggest a new proportional system of voting, and I call it 'One Grand, One Vote'. The richer you are, the more votes you get. What could be simpler than that?

So come on Mr Major. You've got a few bob yourself. Give us 'One Grand, One Vote', and Britain will be quids in on polling day.

☆ I'm not going to condone prostitution. I'd be a hypocrite if I did.

We've all gone with a pro. And any red-blooded male who says he hasn't is either lying, or he's a queer.

But there has to be something wrong with a system that forces headmasters onto the streets, in fishnet stockings, stiletto heels and bright red lipstick.

These men hold the future of our children in their hands. Surely we can pay them a decent living wage.

But hold on a minute. Throwing money at the problem won't solve anything. That's Kinnock's anwer to everything, and it simply doesn't add up.

No. If teachers want a fair day's pay, they should try doing a fair day's work, instead of popping into school for 6 hours a day, 12 weeks a year, then moaning that they're hard up.

Come on sirs! Three out of ten for effort – **could do better.**

★ ★ ★

Ten years ago Willie Whitelaw threatened a short, sharp shock. Well, I've got a shorter, sharper shock of my own that's guaranteed to stop thugs from re-offending.

It's called a bullet – in the head.

So come on Mr Major. You're the *ref*, and we demand a death *penalty!*

It's time **YOU** put these vermins out of **OUR** misery.

I'm backing Britain's bobbies

So the Home Office are considering bigger batons for Britain's bobbies. But do we really need these American style gimmicks on our streets?

Whatever happened to the traditional British bobby? Armed with nothing more than a bicycle, he could command the respect of the entire community.

And in those days you could leave your front doors open.

But you can't seriously expect a workman to do his job without the tools. And no matter how big a stick a policeman wields, it won't stop a bullet from a rapist's gun.

Two wrongs may not make a right, but you must fight fire with fire. There's no smoke without it.

So come on Mr Major. How many more women and children must die before we get the coppers tooled up?

KEEP IT CLEAN

Election time is here and mudslingers are crawling out of the woodwork once again. They tell us that Paddy Ashdown had a brief fling with his secretary several years ago.

So what?

Any politician who says he's never had a bit on the side is either a liar, or a queer. Or both.

Paddy's done the decent thing. Once the whistle was blown he came clean. For that he can hold his head up high.

But what about his wife? Here's a man who leaves his loved one washing dishes and sewing buttons on his shirt while he is out playing the field. *And the monster then has the nerve to ask us for his vote!*

Hang your head in shame, Mr Ashdown. *I'd rather vote for Hitler!*

NOW IT'S THE EURO STOOL

Eurocrat beaurocrats in Brussels are planning a new assault on the British way of life. And this time they want to get their hands on our *Number Twos*.

According to EEC officials *stools*, or turds as they are sometimes known, must all fall in line with tough new European standards of consistency and size.

LOGS

And that means no more sloppy ones or giant logs. From now on British backsides will be expected to produce regulation *Euro-stools*. And according to EEC health chiefs, new poos must be:

★ **FIRM** but not hard.

★ **REGULAR** in consistency and movement.

★ **MID-BROWN** – they must conform to British Standard colour BS06D45.

★ and be about the size of a Mars bar, but pointed at either end.

PIE

Last night Britain's toilet goers were up in arms about the proposed changes.
"This is the last straw", said taxi driver Eddie Johnson, a regular visitor to public toilets in Fulchester city centre. "They've got no business meddling in our dumps", he fumed.

TABLE

Traffic warden Peter Parkinson agreed. "It's like something Hitler would have dreamt up", said Peter, who moves his bowel two or three times a day.

Other countries are also up in arms about the new rules. The French, who drink a lot of thick, black coffee and wine, and who eat onions, traditionally produce a dark coloured (Dulux 'Conker'), loose stool (and aren't fussy about where they drop it).

CHAIR

The Germans, who purely by coincidence started *both* world wars, will also struggle to adapt their droppings. Their stools reflect their breakfasts, resembling raw sausages – very firm and light in colour.

BUREAU

The Italians could also be in trouble, their stringy, tomato smelling, spagetti-like excrement falling well short of the new requirements.

DEXYS

Fulchester Sunnyoak MP Sir Anthony Regents-Park told reporters at a hastily arranged press conference that he would be opposing the new measures. "I will be *passing a motion* in the House of Commons", he quipped before shitting in a bucket for the benefit of photographers.
Pop singer Cliff Richard was last night unavailable for comment.

Eurocrats demand Eurocraps under E.C.'s faeces regulations

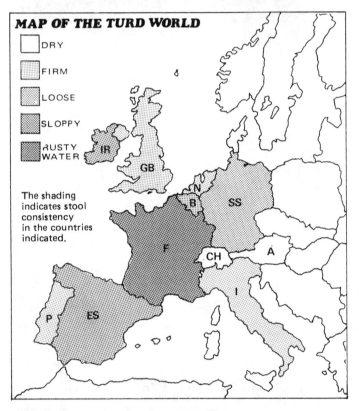

MAP OF THE TURD WORLD

☐ DRY
▨ FIRM
▨ LOOSE
▨ SLOPPY
▨ RUSTY WATER

The shading indicates stool consistency in the countries indicated.

IMPROVING YOUR POOS WILL BEAT BOTTY BLUES

If you're worried about the appearance of *your* stools, here's how you can change them. We asked a leading authority on toilet matters, Dr Branston Pickle of Huddersfield University's Department of Lavatory Studies to compile a simple guide to improving your foulage.

Here's what to do if your stools suffer from any of the following common symptoms.

★ TOO BIG
Eat an orange before every meal, avoid porridge, and try holding a tennis ball between your buttocks for a few hours every day.

★ TOO SLOPPY
Try eating Weetabix *without* milk on it, drink less and eat more peanut butter and treacle.

★ CONSTIPATION
Eat prunes, drink sunflower oil instead of milk in your tea, and try passing stools in unusual and exciting places, like your neighbours garden.

★ TOO DARK IN COLOUR
Try eating white bread instead of brown, and white sugar. Also try to avoid pepper – use salt instead.

★ TOO LIGHT IN COLOUR
Use soya sauce instead of milk in your tea.

★ RABBIT TODS
Aglomerate random or 'buckshot' faeces into a uniform and cohesive block by adding a regular Curly Wurly bar to your diet instead of lunch.

I'VE TURNED THE TAP ON. IS THERE ANY WATER COMING OUT?

NO. THERE MUST BE A KINK IN THE HOSE.

GIRL - YOU REALLY GOT ME NOW. YOU GOT ME SO I DON'T KNOW WHAT I'M DOING...

DR. DM. 92

WHOSE TWOS?

In order to scrape a bit more mileage out of this tedious and juvenile subject, we've compiled a *just for fun* toilet humour game that everyone can play.

STOOLS

Our toilet artist has drawn 4 imaginary stools. We want you to try and guess which of the four famous celebrities pictured might have passed each one. To help you choose we've also compiled an imaginary diet for each celebrity.

ANSWERS

Make a note of which stool you think each star produced, then check your answers with a friend. Or just throw them away. Do what you like with them. We don't care.

Stool A

Stool B

Stool C

Stool D

~ Menu ~
LEE MAJORS

Potato chips
Red meat
Peanut butter
Mollasses
Regular coke
Apple pie

~ Menu ~
VAL DOONICAN

Cheese
White bread
Spam
Sardines
Ritz crackers
Sweetcorn

~ Menu ~
FLOELLA BENJAMIN

Fish
Peas
Ice cream
Wholemeal bread
Salads
Yoghurt

~ Menu ~
MELVYN BRAGG

Caviar
Smoked salmon
Pheasant
M & Ms
Pasta
Trout

BISCUIT RACKET COSTS A PACKET

Biscuit Industry chiefs are facing fresh allegations of overpricing as the storm over biscuit prices continues to gather.

Biscuit retailers have now joined angry consumers who claim that prices are deliberately being maintained at high levels in order to boost profits.

CRACKERS

"It's *crackers*", claimed Doris Halom, head of ABC, the Association of Biscuit Consumers – a voluntary group founded in 1990 to protect the rights of people who buy biscuits. She claimed manufacturers had shoppers over a biscuit *barrel*, and were fig *rolling* it in at the customers' expense".

STUNNERS

And many biscuit shopkeepers are now supporting the fight for lower biscuit prices, among them Ian Gray, managing director of a South East based biscuit retail chain. "Biscuit prices have been increasing way ahead of inflation for the last three years", he told us. "But the price of producing biscuits, in real terms, has actually fallen".

CRUMPET

However a spokesman for the Confederation of British Biscuit Bakers, Sir Huntley Palmer, denied the allegation, "That's *rich* tea coming from him", he told us. "Of course we try to keep the cost to the consumer

Sir Huntley Palmer - under pressure yesterday

down, but at the end of the day we have to make profits, and price increases are inevitable".

MUFFIN

But angry biscuit buyers accused biscuit manufacturers of jammy *dodging* the issue. "False inflationary prices are deliberately being maintained", claimed Doris Halom. "So we in Britain are paying up to twice the price for identical biscuits being sold in America".

ANDY PANDY

When we priced a packet of Maryland Cookies at shops in both Britain and the United States, we found that on average prices were 30% higher on this side of the Atlantic. "That's because they've got more chocolate bits in them", we were told.

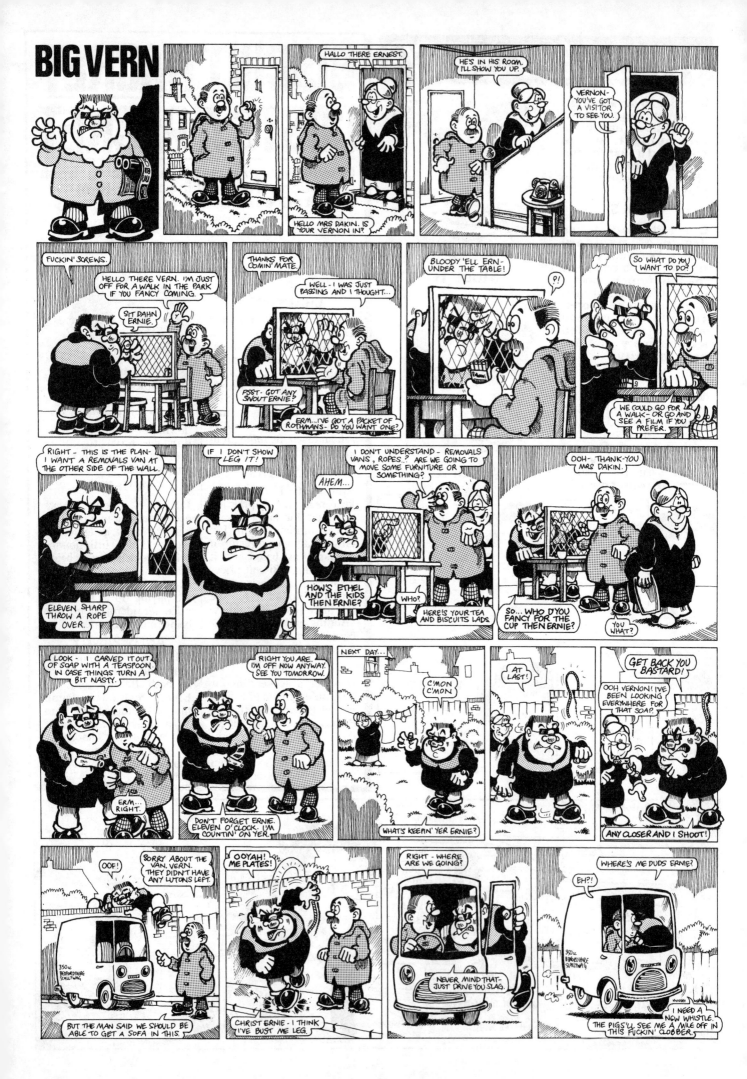

MORE FUN WITH VERN NEXT WEEK.

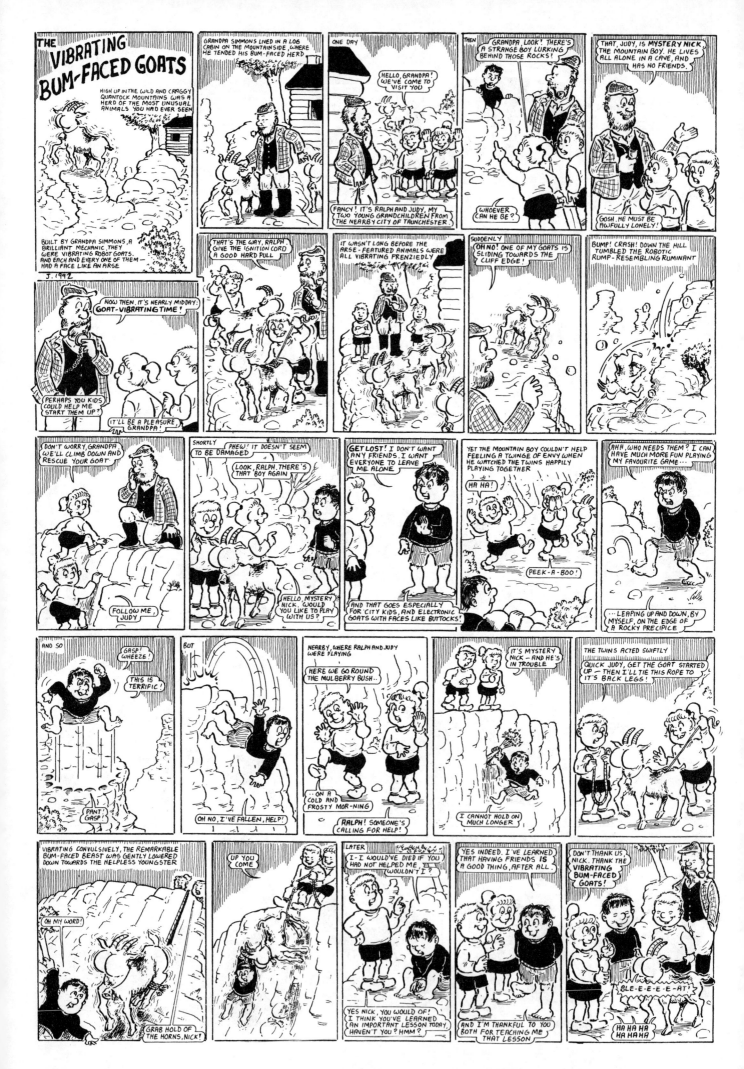

BATTLE OF THE BEN

Who was TV's best Ben? Elton ve

Now that Benny Hill has gone we may never know the answer to the question on a million TV viewers' lips. *Who was the better of the Bennies?*

Was it loveable round faced Benny Hill, adored by viewers worldwide, or was it his arch rival, 'right on' comic, scriptwriter and novelist Ben Elton?

SPARKS

The two comedians were far from friends. After Elton had lashed out at Hill's "sexist" shows, Benny was taken off the air. There can be no doubt that had the pair come face to face after a night of heavy drinking, sparks would have flown.

10cc

But if the telly clowns had come to blows, who'd have had the last laugh?

LUITENANT PIGEON

We asked a doorman at a leading Newcastle nightclub to use his experience to assess the likely outcome of a scrap between the stars. And we're offering you, the readers, an imaginary ringside seat as the two Bennies battle it out.

BEVVY

Picture a quiet pub. Benny Hill has been sitting quietly in the corner surrounded by a bevvy of his TV beauties. Suddenly in walks Ben Elton who has been drinking heavily all evening. Big mouth Ben deliberately starts chatting up Hill's Angels. A row breaks out. After some pushing and shoving a glass gets broken. The landlord orders both comedians to leave, but in the car park their row continues. A crowd gathers, and an ugly scene is developing. Our big fight expert takes up the commentary.

SECONDS OUT ROUND ONE

"A lot depends on who makes the first move. There'll be a lot of pushing and shoving, with both boys baiting their opponent, shouting "Come on fatso", or "Any time, smart arse".

PINT

Elton's got the gift of the gab. As it turned nasty he'd probably try to talk his way out of bother. But Benny Hill means business, and he'd start poking Elton in the chest. If Hill touched Elton's suit, that's when the trouble would start. Elton would lose his rag and lash out. But he'd miss, and Hill would land his first shot – a right hook that catches Elton smack in the mush.

FISH SUPPER

The crowd would go wild, as Elton's glasses fly off. Breaking his opponent's specs would give Hill a big psychological advantage. Elton would blow a fuse. He'd screw up his face, stick out his tongue, and run forward screaming, his arms flailing around like a windmill. He'd batter Benny with a series of lightweight blows. But Hill's a big fella. He'd just grab Elton's head, wrestle him into an armlock, then punch his face with his free hand while half throttling him with the other arm.

CLAW '

Elton realises his only chance is to use Hill's weight against him. He'd claw his way out of the headlock and clench Hill around the waist, desperately trying to unbalance him with an out-

stretched leg. Locked together the pair would stumble around the car park, rolling off car bonnets, with occasional kicks and punches coming from both sides. Suddenly Elton would twist his opponent round, and the big man would lose his footing in some loose gravel, and tumble over, banging his head on a car door as he fell.

SECONDS OUT ROUND TWO

Now Elton is on top. Hill is down, lying flat out in a daze. Elton could win if he takes advantage and puts the boot in. *But he's a gentleman, and he won't fight with his feet, or hit an opponent when he's down.*

SLEDGE

Instead he taunts Hill, skipping around his opponent and beckoning him with a wave of his forefinger. Elton points at his own chin "Come on, big boy. Right there, on me chin". But Elton gets too close, and Hill grabs his leg and pulls it from under him. Suddenly they're both on the floor, rolling back and forward,

scraping, biting and pulling at each other's hair. Hill lands a good punch on Elton's ear, while Elton tries to bite off his opponent's nose. Hill yells and pushes Elton away.

LUMP

Scrambling to his feet, Elton briefly pauses to inspect the damage to his suit. It's a fatal mistake, for he looks up to see Hill charging towards him like a bull, head lowered. Letting out an enormous yell he crashes into Elton's stomach, sending him reeling backwards into a stack of dustbins. Rubbish flies in all directions.

TOFFEE

Elton looks round and sees a beer bottle lying next to him. He grabs it, and rising to his feet he smashes it on a nearby wall. Brandishing the jagged bottleneck in his clenched fist, he glares at Hill. He growls like a ferocious wild animal. Shocked onlookers draw a breath.

FUDGE

Hill responds by tugging a two foot section of rusty down pipe away from the wall. A rusty, jagged bolt protrudes from the shat-

NIES
'sus Hill

tered wall fastening. The pair stand frozen, like lions ready to pounce.

SECONDS OUT
DING A-LING!
FINAL ROUND

Elton makes the first move. He raises his arm, but suddenly he feels a sharp pain as the iron pipe crashes into his wrist sending his weapon flying. Unarmed, he panics as Hill slowly walks towards him.

SHERBET

"Ah, come on Benny. No harm done eh? Lets be mates," he says, but Hill isn't listening. He picks Elton up off the ground by his glitzy lapels, and butts him in the face before throwing him to the ground. Elton, his nose bleeding and his eye swollen, drags himself to his feet, but Hill is straight back at him, punching him – left, right, left, right – until the battered comic crumples and collapses to the ground.

NOUGAT

Hill staggers towards him. Exhausted, he musters one last drop of energy to raise his leg and deliver a final boot to his victim's ribs, before being helped back into the pub by showbiz pals Bob Todd and Henry McGee for a celebration pint.

STRIP

Meanwhile sad loser Ben Elton is helped away by Comic Strip pals, a beaten man.

FIGHT

When we rang Thames TV and asked *if* he'd still been alive and had *somehow* got into a fight with Ben Elton, who did they think would have won, a spokesman refused to comment.

KAJAGOO WHO?

Millions of TV fans have mourned the loss of screen hero Doctor Who since the BBC's controversial decision to axe the long running show.

The legendary sci-fi star had time travelled the Universe in his Tardis since the early sixties. But despite bitter protests from heart broken viewers, Beeb bosses have refused to reinstate the popular programme.

SOLO

But now the Doctor could be saved, thanks to the single handed efforts of a pop star. For Limahl, out of Kajagoogoo, has launched a solo campaign to save the series and has been in touch with BBC bosses in an effort to re-launch the Tardis onto our screen.

BOND

The rumour is that pop idol Limahl has written a new 26 part adventure for the Doctor, and has volunteered to play the starring role.

SMART

According to pals, the singer, whose hit includes 'Too Shy', dreamt up the scheme during a brief lull in his pop career. And they say he is deadly serious in his attempts to save his favourite TV show. "He has been locked away in his garden shed writing the new series for several months. And I believe he's also designed several monsters for the Doctor to deal with", one told us.

CHIPPERFIELD

In the past the Doctor has done battle with the Daleks, the Cybermen, the Yeti and the Sea Devils to name but a few. If Limahl has his way future menaces will include the Tree Monsters, the Kite Heads and the Pan Men. Former Doctor Who's have included Bill Pertwee, William Woolard and Dennis

Limahl (above) and two of the new monsters he has created.

Waterman. But according to one source within the BBC, Limahl has his heart set on making the role his own. "He's even designed a brand new costume and a whole new image for the Doctor", we were told.

ARCHAOS

When we rang the BBC, Esther Rantzen said that they couldn't comment until they had seen the scripts. "We haven't received anything up until yesterday's post", she told us. But Limahl's chances of success are limited. The BBC turned down a similar idea in 1989 when Martin Fry out of ABC offered to take over the Basil Brush Show.

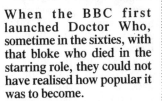

DO YOU KNOW WHO?

When the BBC first launched Doctor Who, sometime in the sixties, with that bloke who died in the starring role, they could not have realised how popular it was to become.

Well here's an opportunity for die-hard fans to test their knowledge of the series by entering our Doctor Who Quiz. And there's a super inflatable Dalek sex doll waiting to be won by whoever sends us the first correct entry.

1. **Doctor Who's time machine the Tardis was disguised as what?**
   a. A tailor's shop
   b. A swimming pool
   c. A police call box.

2. **Which of the following actors has *not* played Doctor Who?**
   a. Patrick Troughton
   b. Peter Cushing
   c. David Niven

3. **Which seventies pop group donned silver costumes to play the Cybermen?**
   a. Mud
   b. Smokie
   c. Showaddywaddy

4. **What is the worst thing about Doctor Who?**
   a. The crappy plots
   b. The awful special effects
   c. The boring bastards who still go on about it all the time, and who go to stupid 'Dr Who Conventions', and who dress up as bloody Daleks and call their children Davros, if they ever get to have any. Which is unlikely.

5. **And I'll tell you what. Blake's Seven was crap as well.**

LetterBox

You've all got tiny cocks

Judging by the overt misogynism that appears in your boysie comic, I can only assume that you all have hang-ups about the size of your cocks and probably feel threatened by females of all ages. Your evident hatred of women makes your comic as low grade as The Sun, The Sport and other papers you pretend to ridicule.

Jenny Marlow, aged 14
Camden Square
London NW3

We're sorry you feel that way Jenny. But cheer up. Your prize letter has won you a free copy of our Fat Slags video – out in November.

Regarding Braintree in Essex (Letterbox, issue 54). I also live in Braintree, Essex. And here's a photograph to prove it. So put *that* in your pipe and smoke it!

C. Palmer
Braintree, Essex

Sir Andrew-Lloyd Weber has just bought a Canaletto from Sotherbys for ten million quid. Well I've just bought a can of lager from Tescos for 39p. Who's the cunt?

E. O'Dross
Reigate

Police often warn old folk to be on their guard against bogus officials who call at their door. Well my mother is 93, but she won't be caught out by the con men. She keeps a pan of chip fat constantly on the boil, and pours it over the head of any caller who cannot prove their identity.

P. Fletcher
Mildenhall

LetterBocks
Viz Commick
P.O. Box 1 PT
Newcastle upon Tyne
NE99 1PT

On the issue of passive smoking, I think it's outrageous that I have to spend over two quid on a packet of tabs when it has been scientifically proved that I am sharing them with some tight fisted gits who've never even bought a box of matches. Isn't it about time these so-called "non-smokers" were made to compensate us honest smokers for passively enjoying *our* fags.

R.V. Toomey
Belfast

Big feet warning

Any young girls thinking of getting married, take a word of advice. *Don't* marry anyone with big feet. If you do your children will have big feet too.

A. Everett
Brighton

I think the police get a raw deal at the hands of the British media. On the one hand society asks them to put themselves at risk in order to protect us from crime. And then we complain the minute they start beating people up, or jailing a few innocent paddies. You can't make an omlette without breaking eggs. Ask any chef. So come on, give Britain's bobbies our backing. They deserve it.

Det. Con. D. Witherspoon
West Midlands C.I.D.

They say that if you shop around you wil always find a bargain. Well I visited a dozen estate agents before buying my house for £275,000. And now it's worth £190,000. So fuck that little theory.

J. Brown
Hammersmith

The other day I sat down with a cup of tea and tried to decide who I'd rather go to bed with: Michelle Pfeifer or Melanie Griffiths. I weighed up the pros and cons of each, taking into account Michelle's curvaceous cat-like figure, Melanie's girlish features and both girl's impressive busts. However, after a couple of hours – and several more cups of tea – I still could not decide between the two.

Could any of your readers help me to decide which of these two Hollywood beauties I would rather go to bed with?

Harold Garratt
Jewbury, Yorks.

Come on then readers. If you were in Mr Garratt's shoes, who would you go to bed with? Send your letter to our usual address.

History repeats itself

It's all very good making jokes about the Germans stealing the deck chairs in holiday resorts, but that is where the rot sets in. Next thing you know they'll be annexing the swimming pool and the whole shennanigans will start all over again.

M. Newell
Essex

Correct me if I'm wrong, but it seems to me that lorry drivers are responsible for a disproportionately high amount of murders in Britain. It's certainly something worth bearing in mind the next time you see them flashing their lights at each other on motorways.

E. Fish
Dartford

Hat off to T.V. chefs

Is it any wonder that the staff in food shops, cafes and restaurants don't wear hats anymore when TV chefs such as Keith Floyd and Lloyd Grossman don't wear hats. I think it's high time people in the catering industry wore hats again.

Mrs A. Burgess
Burford

Why all the concern about falling standards in our schools? I'm pretty thick myself, and I certainly don't want some smart arse fucking student coming along and taking my job in a few years time just cos he's got loads of qualifications. 'Keep 'em thick', that's what I say.

W. Walker
Norwich

Top tips

A TEASPOON placed in a cup on the back seat of your car makes a handy audible gauge for road bump severity.

R. Crabb
Nantwich

CONVINCE dinner guests that you have woodworm in the house by drilling small holes in the arms and legs of your dining chairs.

S. Cooper
Tring

EDGE your lawn into the shape of a pair of trousers then mow it in lines so that from above it looks like a huge pair of green corduroy trousers. Pockets can simply be added by planting small flower beds.

Hapag Lloyd
Runcorn

PRETEND to have dry rot by filling your sub floor void with candy floss.

S. Cooper
Tring

If Nigel Mansell can drive around a race track packed with 200,000 people at speeds of up to 200 miles an hour, how come on my way home from the pub I can't drive through the deserted streets of our town centre at a modest 80 without getting stopped by the police? Is it perhaps because Mr. Mansell is a policeman. I wonder.

S. Hurst
Market Drayton

"You soon begin to realise your children are growing up", a friend told me recently "when their feet get bigger and you have to buy them new shoes".

P. Martin
Southport

ENSURE circular objects such as vases stand centrally on your mantle piece by subtracting the diameter of the object from the length of the mantle piece and dividing by two. Then simply cut a piece of string or nylon fishing cord to that length. Place the cut edge of the string flush to one edge of the mantle piece and then slide the vase or object along it's length until the vase or object abuts the other edge of the string. The string can then be popped into the vase and re-used later should it be moved for any reason.

H. Moleson
Wadebridge

CON passing aeroplane passengers into thinking your house has an outdoor swimming pool by painting a large blue rectangle on your lawn.

Mr Paul
Crawley

MAKE people think they've seen a snake by squirming around your local park in a rolled up carpet with a fork dangling from your mouth and making hissing noises.

T. Dale
Glasgow

They say that the grass is always greener on the other side of the fence. My neighbour would probably disagree. I've just had my entire garden concreted over.

B. Bounty
Rochester

How come a three legged stool stands up, whilst when I saw a leg off a chair it falls over?

A Tetbury
Flamborough

This one isn't as simple as it first looks. Your poser is all to do with gravity, the 'glue' which sticks apples – and chairs – to the floor.
Astronauts unstick this glue by going into space, where they weigh less than a feather, and consequently do not need chairs.
So whilst a stool is merely a tall, thin chair with no back, a three legged chair will always wobble due to the fact that one of its legs is missing.

DON'T waste money on expensive telephone answering machines. When you leave the house simply plug your phone into your video recorder. Not only will it record the callers voice, but you'll also get a television picture of them speaking. Probably.

T. J. Jones
Valenton

OBTAIN the appearance of mice infestation in your home by making small holes in the skirting board and scattering a few currents around the floor.

S. Cooper
Tring

TREAT yourself on birthdays and special occasions by carrying a comfortable chair around with you. When you get tired of carrying the chair you can sit down at any time for a well earned rest.

Gary Bennett
Oxford

SMALL tadpoles, with their tails removed, make tasty (and cheap) cavier substitutes.

D. Tanby
Formby

LET'S NAIL SHED CRIME

Real life Tynesdie crime fighters have come to the rescue of TV Geordie cop come pop singer Jimmy Nail.

Chart topper Nail normally dishes out justice in his role as TV's 'Spender'. But this time Geordie Jim was on the receiving end – of some useful advice from real life Northumbria Police officers.

Police warned tough guy actor Jimmy that his garden shed may be at risk from burglars. "During 1991 there were 9,153 burglaries from garden sheds in the Northumbria police region", a police spokesman told Jimmy. "And my message to shed owners is 'Start thinking now about improving the physical security of garden sheds and other outbuildings".

Real life ex-boozer and former jail bird Jim, now on the right side of the law and happily married with two kids, was happy to take the advice on offer. And with crime on the increase, he recommends that Viz readers do the same.
So here's Spender's Top Ten Tips to protect your garden shed from unwanted visitors this summer.

'SPENDER' MINUTE STUDYING THESE 10 SHED SECURITY TIPS

1. Fit a hasp with concealed screws and a strong padlock.

2. Fit window locks too.

3. Consider using reinforced glass in shed windows.

4. Don't leave tools in the shed which might be used to burgle your house.

5. Fit extra locks to your shed then *use them*, even if you're only nipping out of your shed for a few moments.

6. If you go away, ask a neighbour to keep an eye on your shed.

7. If you leave valuables in your shed, like a mountain bike, mark it with your postcode so it can be identified.

8. Install security lights and movement detectors around your shed.

9. Surround your shed with a fence, AND a thorny hedge for extra protection.

10. Don't allow shrubs and bushes around your shed to overgrow, as this provides cover for a shed thief to work behind.

IT'S SILLY SAUSAGE

IT'S TRUE. IF YOU SWALLOW CHEWING GUM IT STICKS TO YOUR INSIDES AND KILLS YOU.

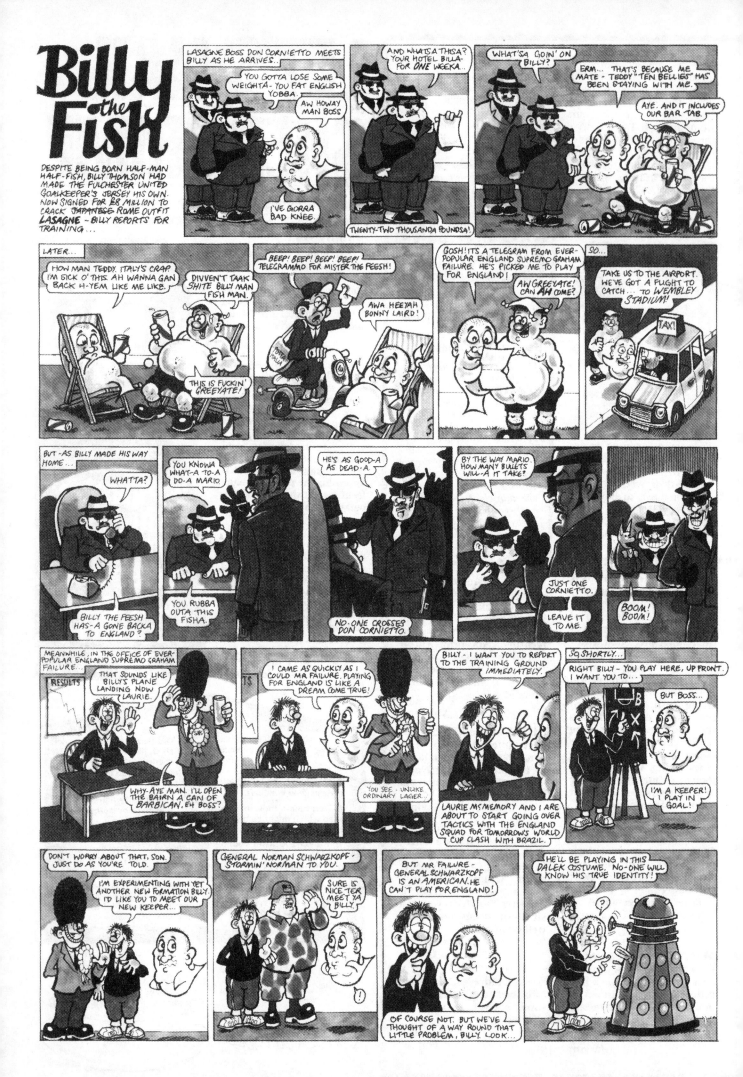

WE FIND HITLER'S WANK MAGS

A pile of dirty books belonging to Hitler have been discovered buried in a shallow grave in former Russian occupied Berlin.

The porno mags, which were in a plastic bag, were previously believed to have been destroyed by Hitler's faithful SS guard shortly after the Fuhrer's death.

KREMLIN

But Russian military records, only just made public by the Kremlin, revealed that the male interest mags, which Hitler carried with him throughout the war, were secretly buried on Stalin's orders after the Russian leader had looked at them for a bit.

PENTAGON

If scientific tests on the pages of the magazines – some of which were stuck together – confirm that they were Hitler's, it will reinforce the popular theory that towards the end of the war the Fuhrer had become obsessed with pornographic material.

HITLER - secret stash

Experts believe that Hitler intended to harness pornography for use as a weapon against the allies, and that in 1945 Nazi scientists were on the verge of inventing the *dirty video* – a breakthrough that could have changed the outcome of the war. For Hitler had planned to bombard Britain with copies of his new secret weapon, hoping that triple X hardcore porn videos, featuring red hot explicit sex action, would distract the British population sufficiently to tilt the balance of power in Germany's favour.

We offered Hitler's dirty magazines to The Sunday Times, cos that's that sort of shit they buy, but they haven't rang us back yet.

GOEBBELS - Nazi number two.

Dr Ludmila Fredrikson of the Swedish Institute of Advanced Sexual Research believes that Hitler's unique medical condition – he is believed to have had only one testicle – could account for his apparent obsession.

DODECOHEDRON

"A one nutted person would indeed have an enormous appetite for filth", she told us.

THE MYSTERY OF SHINGLE COVE

For years mystery and rumour have surrounded the sudden evacuation of the village of Shingle Cove on the Suffolk coast in November, 1944.

And despite official denials, to this day locals still believe that their village was the target of Hitler's first experimental 'porn warfare' attack.

TRAPEZIUM

The story goes that on that cold winters night German planes flew overhead and dropped thousands of propaganda leaflets on the small fishing community. But they were no ordinary propaganda leaflets that rained down onto the beach, like giant snowflakes in a swirling blizzard. As one local who claims to have witnessed the attack recalls.

CLOWNS

"They were pictures of the Queen Mother, with no clothes on", Fred Gutteridge, now 78, told us.

Despite his advancing years, and the onset of incontinence, Fred still vividly recalls the dirty pamphlets that fell from the sky. "They were disgusting. She was completely naked, in all sorts of positions. Flap shots, the lot".

BEARDED LADY

On another page a ficticious newspaper headline told how Princess Di had worked in Amsterdam as a prostitute, and regularly had sex with four men at once on a filthy mattress.

HARDCORE

Military analysts believe that Hitler's propaganda chiefs had used hardcore Swedish models to pose for disgusting and lewd photographs and then superimposed the Queen Mum's head on top.

QUEEN MUM - Filthy pictures

The pamphlet was designed to shock the British public and lower vital wartime morale.

Fred recalls how the army quickly sealed off the village and confiscated all the pamphlets. "They took them all to some woods nearby and burnt them", he told us.

BALLAST

The mystery of Shingle Cove will remain unsolved until the year 2500 when official War Office files on the incident are opened to the public.

Gracie and Vera in Nazi porno shocker

Sex mad Hitler had drawn up detailed plans of what he intended to do with Britain if he had won the war.

And, according to Kremlin war records released this week, one of the filthy minded Nazi's top priorities was to make disgusting porno videos starring Vera Lynn and Gracie Fields.

SEX BOMB - Hitler's secret weapon - the triple 'X' porno movie

The would-be porn king planned to lure the British songbirds into a career in blue movies, by offering them tons of Nazi gold. And together with his right hand man Goebbels, Hitler had already written several scripts in which Lynn and Fields, the darlings of the British Forces, were expected to perform;

* **TOPLESS**
* **GIRL ON GIRL**
* and **HAMBURGER SHOTS**

However, Hitler's adult video plans, together with his plan for world domination, were scuppered when he lost the war.

T.V. MOTSON'S SUNKEN TREASURE HOPES SINK

Plans for a treasure hunting expedition to the Carribean lead by BBC football commentator John Motson have run aground.

Motson had planned to set sail with a crew of BBC Sport colleagues and go in search of sunken treasure worth millions of pounds. But after months of planning Motson has had to cancel the expedition which has been besieged by problems throughout.

DAVID VINE - dropped out

Some sunken treasure yesterday

TREASURE

The first blow came when Match Of The Day colleagues accused Motson of *forging* a treasure map which he claimed showed the whereabouts of buried Spanish gold.

DARLING

"His map, which was supposed to be 300 years old, was drawn in felt pen on the back of BBC notepaper", one colleague told us.

PETAL

A further set back came when Motson was unable to hire a boat for his 6,000 mile round journey, as the 44 year old commentator has no sailing experience whatsoever.

DUCKY

And the final blow came when BBC bosses refused Motson six months off work, due to the forthcoming Olympic Games.

LAMB CHOPS

Motson had already seen three of his intended crew members drop out due to work commitments. Fellow football commentator Barry Davies, snooker anchor man David Vine and football analyst Trevor Brooking had been Motson's first choice of shipmates. But despite frantic phone calls to other colleagues, and offers of substantial amounts of gold, he was unable to find replacements.

BASIL BRUSH

However one BBC insider told us that Motson, who inherited the BBC's football commentary crown from David Coleman, has not given up entirely, and may launch another expedition early next year, possibly using advanced technology to help in his search for treasure.

Colleagues in the Match of The Day office report that Motson has spent several afternoons working on plans for a 'Special Underwater Mini-Submarine' that will enable him to scour the sea bed for sunken treasure.

HELLO.

THAT'S MIGHTY BIG TALK.

SPOT the ROYAL American TV COP

Every week we ask a member of the Royal Family to disguise themself as an American TV cop.

Can you identify this week's mystery Royal TV cop look-a-like? Here's a clue:

This veteran Royal is everyone's favourite granny, but in her TV Cop disguise there's *fat* chance of her getting *fired*.

If you think you know the answers, write the name of the Royal and the TV cop on the back of a postcard and send it to: Viz Royalty American TV Cop, ...). Box 1PT, N... IPT. The first correct entry out of the hat will win our fabulous first prize – Hi Fi equipment to the value of your choice from any branch of *Richer Sounds*. And an electric cooker.

TURN TO PAGE 125 FOR THE ANSWER

BOND GOES BUST

Former screen Bond star and TV Templar 'Saint' actor Roger Moore is rumoured to be in financial trouble after investing his movie millions in a failed business venture.

Moore, 60, who played suave, smooth talking '007' in a string of blockbuster movies ploughed profits from his Bond appearances into a taxi company while living in southern Spain. Friends believe he was trying to emulate original Bond star and showbiz pal Sean Connery, whose multi-million pound business interests include a private bank and U.S. property company.

IVANHOE

But according to pals Moore's scheme has run aground, leaving TV's former knight in armour 'Ivanhoe' high and dry.

ROBIN HOOD

Moore set up the taxi company in Marbella where he lived, investing in a private hire license and a five seater cab. Trading as '007 Taxis' he operated the service in the hills around his home in order to make extra money during breaks between movie making. According to locals the business got off to a flying start.

WILLIAM TELL

"Roger seemed to keep very busy, especially at weekends, driving people into town, to restaurants and bars, and picking them up in the evenings", we were told. "Adverts for his taxi appeared in phone boxes all around the town. Roger even had some pens made with '007 Taxis' and the phone number written on the side".

1812

But as a former neighbour of the star explained, things began to go sour. "A lot of the time Roger wasn't in, he'd be away making a film, so the phone would ring and ring and no-one would answer it. After a while people gave up trying".

Another problem was Moore's lack of knowledge of the area. Having only lived in Marbella for a couple of months he was unfamiliar with many of the local roads, and often took hours rather than minutes to arrive. "On one occasion I booked him to pick me up at 8pm. Eventually he arrived at ten minutes past midnight, having driven for miles trying to find my house. He must have spent a fortune on petrol, but in the end he only charged me about two pounds", another local told us. "He can't have been making money".

1066

Another former fare told us that Moore often undercharged. "A lot of taxi drivers take you for a ride, but Roger was just the opposite. Often, if you didn't have the right change, he'd let you off the fare".

007~licensed to carry five passengers

Inevitably, Moore had to call in the accountants, and 007 Taxis was closed. The car was sold to help pay off debts, but sources close to the star say some bills remain unpaid, and Moore has since moved out of his million pound villa.

AGINCOURT

Ironically, Moore is not the first James Bond actor to run into off screen business difficulties. A hardware shop opened in Walsall by George Lazenby folded due to competition from several large, out-of-town D.I.Y. stores. At the time Lazenby was quoted as saying that the quality of service to the customer would suffer if the trend away from high street hardware retailers continued.

Bond star Saint actor Moore as TV's Ivanhoe.

"I am simply unable to compete with the bulk buying of the giants and the kind of discounts they can offer", he told reporters at his closing down sale.

FLODDEN FIELD

More recent Bond star business ventures have proven to be more durable. A hot dog stand opened by actor Timothy Dalton in Covent Garden proved so successful that the former RSC man has just opened four new ones in and around central London.

SPOT the STAR

Here's a fun-to-enter competition for all you star spotters out there. We've disguised some well known celebrities. Can you spot who they are?

Send your answers, on a post card, to 'Viz Crudely Disguised Celebrity Recognition Competition, P.O. Box 1PT, Newcastle upon Tyne, NE99 1PT. The first correct entry drawn out of the hat on 1st February 1993 will receive our first prize – a guided tour of the homes of the stars, with full commentary and including a visit to the moon.

The competition is not open to former Blue Peter presenters, their friends, relatives or dogs. We reserve the right to forget about the competition completely and throw all entries in the bin.

THE ANSWERS TO THIS ENTHRALLING COMPETITION ARE SUPPOSED TO BE ON PAGE 125.

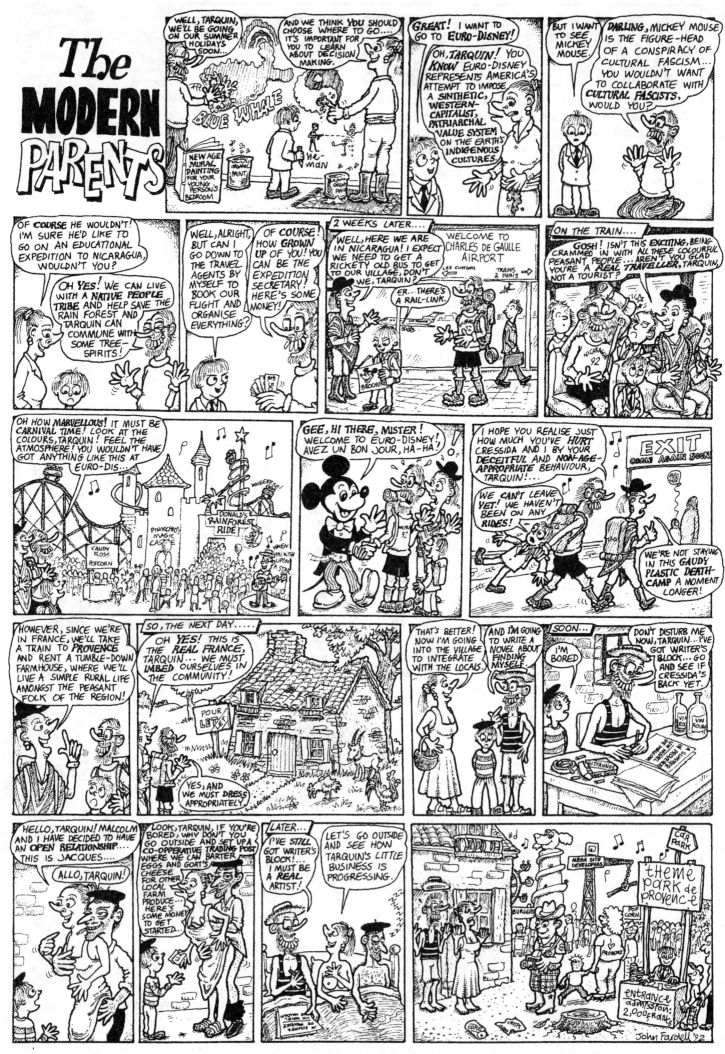

NOEL'S ARK!

Telly superstar Noel Edmunds plans to take a page out of God's book in a dramatic one man bid to save London Zoo.

For the tidy bearded TV host plans to build a giant ark – big enough for all the zoo's ten thousand animals. And like the Bible's Noah, telly's Noel plans to march the animals into his ark two by two when the zoo closes later this year.

ANIMALS

Edmunds launched his spectacular rescue plan in the wake of news that many animals may be destroyed when the zoo's gates finally close. And the game show king's ambitious ark project could mean salvation for thousands of helpless animals, including lions, zebras and giraffes.

But, weather permitting, the dare devil former DJ is determined to go ahead. And officials at London Zoo were cautiously optimistic in their response to the rescue plan. "Anything that will help publicise the plight of homeless animals and help to guarantee their future survival is to be welcomed", one told us.

MALTREATMENT

Naturalist, author and part time zoo keeper Gerald Durrell, a renowned critic of animal maltreatment, was surprisingly unimpressed by Edmunds eleventh hour bid

Animal addict Noel's late, late mercy bid

to save London Zoo. Durrell, who's got a grey beard and married an American bird, a bit like Linda McCartney, refused to comment when we rang him at his Jersey home.

Fellow celebrity zoo owner Lord something or other, the randy one who inherited the lions of Longleat the other week, wasn't available for comment.

FISH

And when we rang Jaques Cousteau for a comment his secretary told us he only talks about fish.

So sad - a homeless monkey

Noel's nautical mercy dash will be one of the most daring and spectacular animal rescue operations in maritime zoo history. And unlike the light hearted game show's which he hosts on our TV screens, Noel is taking his rescue bid *deadly* serious.

LINDISFARNE

"He's read the Bible over and over again, and plans to follow Noah's example down to the last detail", one TV insider told us. But other colleagues at the BBC expressed concerns about the scheme.

TYGERS OF PANTANG

"As I recall Noah's ark relied on heavy rainfall raising the water level sufficiently to set it afloat", said weatherman Michael Fish. "I find it highly unlikely, especially in the current climate, that enough rain will fall on London zoo to launch a giant ark".

SELFISH STARS TURN BACKS ON BEASTS

According to their publicists the top stars will always go out of their way to help a worthy cause.

Whether it's Live Aid, Aids Awareness, Comic Relief or Telethon, there's always a host of famous faces eager to jump on the charity bandwaggon.

PUBLICITY

But away from the glare of publicity, just how kind hearted are the stars? We decided to find out by asking a few well known celebrities whether *they* would be willing to help save the poor, homeless animals of London Zoo.

DAVISON - TV vet

Our first call was to TV vet **PETER DAVIDSON**, star of All Creatures Great and Small. On screen he's on call 24 hours a day to help farm

animals in the Yorkshire Dales. But in real life it was a different story.

GIRAFFES

When we asked whether Davidson would be prepared to provide a home for the zoo's giraffes, and some camels, he flatly refused. "I am a busy man. Please stop wasting my time", he told us.

CHARITY

Big hearted strong man **GEOFF CAPES** is known as the Gentle Giant, and regularly attends charity sports events. But sadly, we have to report that Geoff's gentle caring attitude does not extend to the animals in London Zoo.

BEARS

We asked the World's former Strongest Man whether he could look after a few bears when the zoo closes. We pointed out that these could easily be accommodated in a small pit dug in his back garden.

"I can't keep bears in my garden. It would be illegal",

CAPES - TV strong man

stormed the former policeman. "I could probably look after a couple of budgies, but it would be difficult for me to feed them regularly, especially at Christmas when I'm away doing pantomime", he added.

REDSKINS

Rock superstar **BONO** probably owns a string of houses across the world. And probably has acres of gardens to spare in every one. Surely room for some lions, or perhaps some monkeys, you'd have thought. But no. It seems that big mouth Bono would rather see them destroyed.

"Looking after wild animals is a specialist job", said a

'PAY UP OR SHUT UP!'

American singer songwriter Barry Manilow has sent his number one fan a bill for $28,000 after he caught her singing one of his songs.

Gloria Adams, 53, was in her local delicatessen buying soda pop and pretzels when Manilow popped out from behind a display stand and accused her of humming 'Copa Cobana'.

ROYALTY

Stunned Gloria asked Manilow for his autograph, but all he gave her was a demand for an on-the-spot royalty payment for her use of his song.

LAYERS

After fainting Miss Adams awoke in hospital only to find Manilow's lawyers waiting at her bedside with a court

EXCLUSIVE

Beaky Baz slaps a Copa CoBAN on Gloria

summons for non-payment of the $28,000 fee. And now Gloria, a Manilow fan for twenty years, could lose her home if she cannot find the money.

While millionaire Manilow (left) wears a flouncy shirt, former fan Gloria faces financial ruin and homelessness.

"I don't know what I'm going to do", she told American Knobcheese magazine. "I just pray to God that I won't have to go to prison".

HUMMING

However, a leading music industry lawyer confirmed that Manilow, or any other musician, is quite within their rights to charge royalties from anyone they hear singing, humming or whistling one of their songs in public.

STINKING

"If Barry Manilow overheard this lady humming 'Copa Cobana' in a public place, then as the copyright owner he is entitled to demand a royalty fee. It is his song, to it's entirely up to him what he charges. I'm afraid that if the lady can't

afford to pay, she will simply have to go to prison for a very long time".

REEKING

It is very uncommon for artists to pursue such claims in Britain, although one well publicised case involved ex-Beatle Paul McCartney. During a seventies concert by his band Wings, McCartney invited the entire audience to join him for an encore singing 'Mull of Kintyre', which they did. But the moment the huge crown left the stadium they were stopped by mean McCartney's lawyers who demanded a cash payment of £7.50 from every member of the crowd for the rights to sing his song.

BONO - Pop big mouth

SAVILLE - TV's Mr Fix It

spokesman for U2's record company. "I'm sure Bono would like to help in some other way if he could", we were told. Little consolation for the poor, teary eyed monkeys with nowhere to go, and no-one to care.

ELTON - Comedy big mouth

Motormouth comic **BEN ELTON** is quick to tell us how we should save the environment. But does he practice what he preaches?
"No", snapped Ben when we asked him if he wanted a penguin.

RAIDERS

Veteran fund raiser **JIMMY SAVILE** has raised millions through his marathon efforts

for charity. But when we asked Uncle Jim to 'fix it' for two rinoceroses and an elephant to live in his posh London apartment the golden oldie almost choked on his cigar.
"Eurgn-eugn-eugh! You must be kidding, guys n' gals!", he replied.

DOLPHINS

Out of over two dozen celebrities who we contacted, only one, **RODNEY BEWES**, was willing to accommodate animals from the zoo. "I could probably manage something, as long as it wasn't too big", he told us.

SEAHAWKS

And so, twenty five years since hanging was abolished in Britain, hundreds of innocent little animals face the death penalty – a sentence passed on them by the heartless stars of showbusiness. A chilling thought to bear in mind next time you turn on your television.

FIREBALL DI'S HUMAN TORCH TERROR!

By the gardener who saved her life

A former Buckingham Palace gardener who helped save the Princess of Wales' life during one of her many suicide attempts has come forward to reveal all about the Royal marriage bust up.

And he hopes that by telling his side of the story he may, in some way, earn lots of money.

HORRIFIC

Reg Molesworth personally witnessed one of Diana's most horrific attempts on her life. And if it wasn't for his brave actions the Princess of Wales would not be alive today.

PETROL

"I was working in the garden one afternoon when Diana marched out onto the lawn carrying a can of petrol. Next thing I know she starts pouring it over her head. Then she sits down, gets out a match, and ...*whoof!* She was away".

SMOKE

Reg fought through clouds of thick black smoke to get to the burning Royal. "The heat was incredible, and I had to keep low to avoid the fumes, but I eventually got close enough to pour water on her with my watering can".

SMOKE AGAIN

After the flames subsided Reg and other gardening staff hosed the Princess down with a sprinkler before Di was whisked away to hospital for emergency treatment. "There was a lot of smoke damage, but otherwise she was okay. Luckily she avoided more serious injury because she had been wearing a flame retardent blouse".

PRINCESS

This was just one of dozens of similar attempts which the Princess made on her life while Reg was working at the Palace. "The chef caught her with her head in the oven so many times he had to switch

to using a microwave. And anything sharp had to be kept under lock and key. Diana's bedroom was like a prison cell, just bare walls, a bunk bed and a bucket in the corner for the call of nature. They even took her shoes off her in case she tried to swallow them".

ALLEGRO

Reg places blame for the Royal marriage rift squarely on Charles' shoulders. "It was obvious to anyone working at the Palace that the poor girl, to put it bluntly, wasn't *getting any*. He was always away, and when he was around they'd use separate bedrooms. Many's the time she'd be wandering about the garden in a skimpy frock, eyeing up the gardeners. One time I was doing a bit of weeding when I heard her come up behind me. I could feel her eyes staring at my arse. I thought 'Ello what's this?'. But I had to ignore her. It would have been more than my jobs worth to give her one, I can tell you.

MARINA

Mind you. I'm not kidding. If she hadn't been the Princess of Wales I'd have had her in

my potting shed any day of the week."

MAESTRO

Reg sees little hope of reconciliation between Di and the House of Windsor. Having fallen out with the Royals himself, he knows from experience how unforgiving the Queen and her family can be.

MONTEGO

"You just can't talk to the Queen. She wants everything her own way. And being the Queen, you can be bloody sure she gets it. If I planted some flowers and they were the wrong colour, quick as a flash she'd be out that door screamin' blue murder. I've done plenty of gardens in my time, but that Queen is a bugger to work for, I can tell you".

BOTANY

According to Reg, he was personally dismissed by Her Majesty after a row over the Royal corgis.
"I was sick of cleaning up their shit off the lawn", he told us. "Every fucking day there'd be another bucket full. So one day I said to her 'How would you like it if my kids came round and shat on

Fire rescue hero Reg, above, and the tragic Princess he saved.

your carpet?' That was it. She blew a fuse, and straight away I was out on me arse".

ZOOLOGY

Reg plans to use a detailed diary which he kept during his time at the Palace to write a book revealing the real life Royal dramas that go on behind closed doors. And he's already had one serious enquiry from a leading Sunday newspaper interested in serialising the book.

GENETICS

We would like to point out that Mr Molesworth has received no form of payment whatsoever from this magazine, although we did say we'd send him a cheque next week.

'I CAN SAVE DI'S MARRIAGE'

Joe Kinghorn displaying one of his many caravans yesterday

A Bridlington tradesman yesterday stepped forward and threw a lifeline which could save the Prince and Princess of Wales' marriage from crashing on the rocks.

Joe Kinghorn believes that a caravan holiday could be just the ticket to bring the feuding Royals back together.

TURMOIL

Local trader Joe was genuinely upset when he read reports that the Royal marriage was in turmoil. "I'm a big fan of the Royals, they do a marvellous job, and I have every sympathy for Charles and Di. I realise the pressures they must be under".

CARAVAN

"What they really need is to get away from it all – a complete break. And, what better way to do that than with a caravan", said Joe, Managing Director of Bridlington based Coastal Caravan Sales (UK) Ltd.

"With a caravan in tow Britain becomes your back garden. Every day you can enjoy a different view from your kitchen window. In a word it gives you freedom – freedom to go wherever you please".

LAKES

Joe believes a fortnight or so in the Lakes, or perhaps just the odd weekend away together would give Charles and Di vital breathing space, and a chance to patch up their differences.

RIVERS

"A lot of my customers have similar problems", Joe told us. "I get people in my showroom fighting like cats and dogs. But generally speaking it's the ones who buy the caravans who end up smiling. There's a strange, romantic kind of magic about a caravan, and they're not as expensive as you might think".

STREAMS

Joe has already written to the Palace enclosing a colour brochure and a price list of caravans currently in stock. "I think I've got something for everyone. From the latest, fully equipped luxury models – a real home from home, to the smaller, more compact vehicles. With full credit facilities available – subject to status".

So far Joe has heard nothing from the Prince of Wales, but he is confidently expecting a call. "I quoted him the current list prices, but for a quick sale I would obviously be willing to do a deal on that", said Joe.

Fergie clashes with Queen over telly

The Queen - Fisticuffs with Fergie

The Duchess of York's marriage split with Prince Andrew looks set to end in an undignified slagging match between Fergie and the Palace.

Already the Queen has snubbed the Duchess by banning her from the Palace. And there are even reports of violence between Fergie and her Royal mother-in-law.

FLARED

Former Palace gardener Reg Molesworth confirmed that tempers had flared during a recent visit by Fergie.

BELL BOTTOMED

"I think she'd come back to get her telly and a few of her other things. Next thing I knew there was shouting and screaming and the two of them were at it like cats and dogs. They were scratching and tugging at each others hair. Eventually Palace bodyguards pulled the Queen off, but she was furious, and told Fergie she would finish it next time she saw her".

DRAIN PIPED

Meanwhile Andrew has been in touch with Palace solicitors over unpaid phone bills at the Duke and Duchesses South York home. Since packing her bags Fergie has refused to contribute towards the unpaid bills, thought to total around £300. Andrew insists that the Duchess was responsible for at least three quarters of the calls made.

VIZ READERS BACK ANDY

Viz readers have voted 8 to 2 in favour of Prince Andrew in a recent poll to find out who is to blame for the York's marriage break up.

We asked readers whether the burden of responsibility for the break down in the marriage lay at Andrew's feet, or whether Fergie was at fault, because it was obvious right from the beginning that she was a bit of a tart and not right for our Andy.

We also took the opportunity to ask readers whether they thought Andrew should re-marry quickly on the rebound, take his time and choose the right partner, or say 'What the hell' and play the field a bit, making a bit of hay while the sun shines and generally giving the dog a bone.

And surprisingly, 70 per cent of readers plumped for the latter.

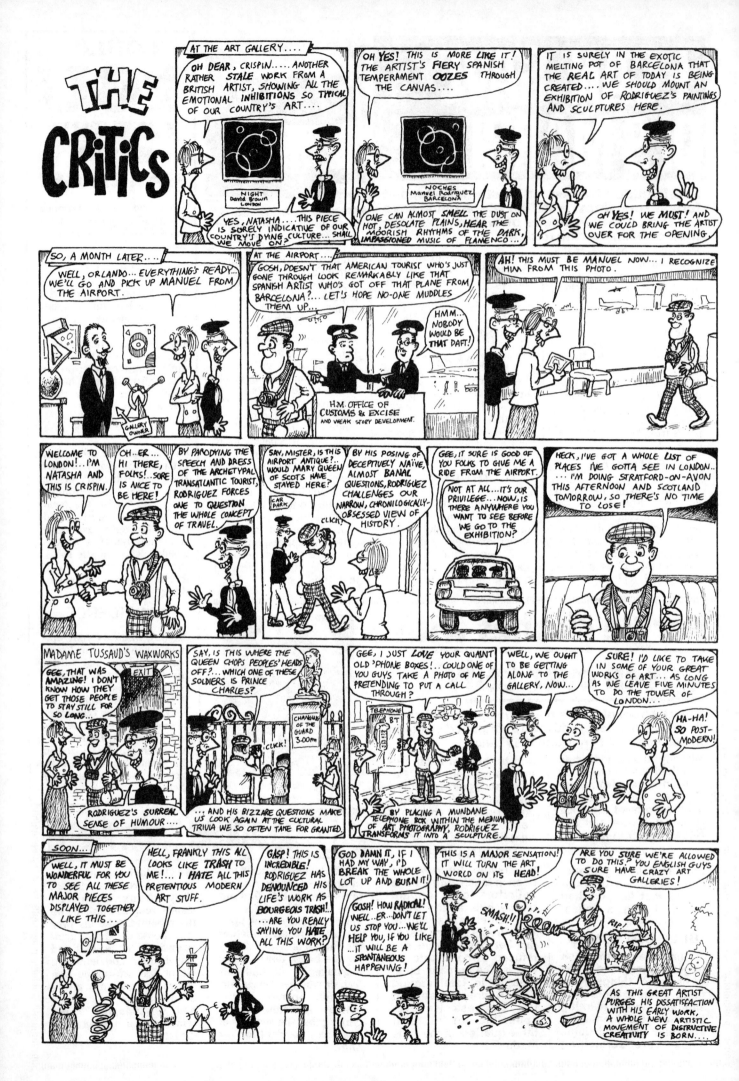

We find Hitler and Robert Maxwell

World War Two villain Adolf Hitler is *ALIVE* and living in Cleethorpes together with Daily Mirror billionaire pension fraudster Robert Maxwell, according to a confused old lady who claims to have seen the couple leaving a flat together in the town.

According to Doris Wardrobe, who is 97 and lives in a retirement home overlooking the beach, the couple, both of whom were presumed dead by the authorities, regularly walk arm in arm together on the seafront. "They appear to be very close", Mrs Wardrobe told us.

LUXURY

Mrs Wardrobe claims to have seen the couple on several occasions coming and going from a luxury £60,000 flat opposite her bedroom window. She told us that Hitler and Maxwell had been living there for several months. "They keep themselves to themselves, and seem like the quiet types", she told us. However she also spoke of late night rows. "On one occasion Marilyn Monroe arrived at the flat late at night. There was an enormous row. By the sound of it Hitler had been going out with her before he met

Robert Maxwell. Mr Maxwell wasn't too pleased to see Hitler's 'ex' turn up on the doorstep. There was a bit of crockery broken that night I can tell you." The situation was resolved and according to Mrs Wardrobe, Monroe left in a taxi at about 5am, accompanied by John F. Kennedy.

MILLIONS

When we called at the flat to accuse Hitler of war crimes and confront Maxwell about the Mirror Group pension fund's missing millions, a young man in his twenties opened the door. "I'm afraid Hitler and Robert Maxwell don't live here", he told us.

MISTAKEN

Last night Mrs Wardrobe admitted she may have been mistaken. "Hitler and Robert Maxwell must be staying in the Grand Hotel, just round the corner", she said.

CHRIST ON A BIKE

A Shrewsbury man believes he may have discovered a motor scooter which originally belonged to Jesus.

Alfred Hepplewhite, 82, believes the bike, which he found buried amidst weeds on allotment near his home, was originally used by Christ to 'get around' during his time on Earth.

BIKE

And now Mr Hepplewhite is using the bike himself, to travel in and around the Shrewsbury area preaching God's word, and also doing his shopping.

SLAG

"Although there is no clear or specific reference to Christ riding a bike in the Bible, the whole book is such a load of twaddle that

you can more-or-less read anything you want into it", a Church spokesman told us yesterday.

GARDENER DIGS PLANT

ITN Newscaster Andrew Gardener yesterday paid tribute to former Led Zeppelin front man Robert Plant.

ZEPPELIN

"I haven't heard much of his recent stuff, but my kids were fans of Led Zeppelin. I quite liked Stairway To Heaven", said Andrew yesterday.

Meanwhile millionaire Plant, whose subsequent solo hits have included Big Log, was out of the country and unavailable for comment according to a spokesman for his record company.

LETTERBOX

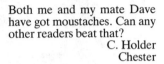

LetterBocks
Viz Commick
P.O. Box 1 PT
Newcasle upon Tyne
NE99 1PT

Come clean Cliff!

It is a scientific fact that even in a celibate male human being the reproductive organ *must* ejaculate regularly, either by means of physical masturbation or nocturnal emissions known as 'wet dreams', in order to rid the body of the sperm which it produces. I should know, because I'm a doctor. So come on Cliff, which is it? One off the wrist or sticky bedclothes?

Dr. I. Halibut
London NW1

Our cocks

Jenny Marlow is right when she says you're all hung up about the size of your darling danglers (Letterbox, issue 55). But then all six year old boys have small cocks, don't they?

Rachel Baldwin
(also aged 14)
London SW12

Other side of the coin

Dear me, hasn't young Jenny Marlow (Letterbox, issue 55) got her pre-pubescent knickers in a knot! I'm sure I speak for the majority of Viz readers when I say we don't hate *all* women, just the fat, ugly, feminist variety. And while I cannot speak for the Viz staff about the size of their cocks – mine's right juicy whopper! In fact I think these feminists' problem is that they're all so ugly they never get a good seeing to.

So come on Viz readers. Drink 15 pints of lager, put a bag on their heads (and one on yours in case hers falls off) and give a fat, ugly feminist a good *rogering!* That ought to cheer the miserable cows up a bit.

A. Reactionary
Liverpool

I have taken drugs, and I also cheat on my girlfriend whenever I'm away from home. Does this qualify me for the British Olympic team in 1996?

T. Organ
Edinburgh

Well spotted

If P.C. Barnett (Jack Black, issue 55) managed to ignite a zeppelin containing *helium*, his scientific talents would have been better employed in the 'Frankenstien's Cock' section of your comic. Helium does not ignite, unlike hydrogen which it replaced in airships some years ago.

Mike Galvin M.Sc.
Erdington

*Congratulations to Mike, and also Bob McDonald, Mike Sutton and P. Blount, all of whom made the same observation.
*Here's another little competition that's open to **all** eagle-eyed readers, not just pedantic bastards who did chemistry 'O' level. In **this** issue, as well as all the usual jokes, we've included a **new** one. Can you spot it? The first person to spot it wins a £5,000 fitted kitchen and a holiday for two in the Canary Islands. And a toaster.*

They say you're as old as you feel. Well, I feel like I did when I was 12. Can I claim Child Benefit on top of my pension?

Bishop Stortford
Bishops Stortford

I'm in favour of the 24 hour clock. Imagine how much more we could get done in a day, and still have a lie in to boot!

Mr Loudhead
Cheadle Hume

Give the girl a chance

I wish people would give Fergie a chance, instead of criticising her the minute she pisses off to the South of France with some Texan slap head and all our loot.

N. Quazar
Godalming

Caravans are a menace on the roads in summer, causing delays for millions of normal motorists. I think it's about time they increased Road Tax on a caravan to £500. Perhaps then these idiots would think twice before deciding to spend their holidays stuck in the same room as their kids, and crapping in a bucket.

T. Lawrence
Birmingham

My young son said he was having a 'Pop Tart' for breakfast. Imagine my surprise when I came downstairs to find TV celebrity Paula Yates sitting on the breakfast table. Do I win £5?

Mrs B. Hearn
Droitwich

Both me and my mate Dave have got moustaches. Can any other readers beat that?

C. Holder
Chester

*Are you a member of a group of two or more people all of whom have moustaches? Or maybe both you and your neighbour have a beard, or metal rimmed glasses. Whatever your group coincidental situation, write and let us know at the usual address. There's a crisp twenty-five pound note for the best letter we receive.

I really can't see the need for all this fuss about corn circles. On a farm near to where I live the aliens have cut down all the crops, rolled them into enormous cylinder shapes, and stacked them all neatly at the side of the fields. None of the local residents, including myself, have felt it necessary to bat an eyelid.

Mr J. Bright
Sheppey, Kent

Sausage turd arse conundrum

When I eat a sausage, wait 24 hours then sit on the toilet, a turd comes out of my bottom. Why then, when I eat a turd, and sit on the toilet 24 hours later a sausage does not come out of my arse?

S. Bowyer
Trowbridge

This is the age of the *battery* train!

Britain's trains should run on batteries — like torches. So says controversial seventies kids' TV newsreader John Craven.

Craven, now 47, believes that battery powered trains would be a boost for Britain, and claims that they'd be quick, clean and environmentally friendly. And the former 'Newsround' presenter has estimated that battery operated expresses travelling at 200 miles an hour could cut journey times by up to two hours.

BATTERY

Craven's brainwave came about when he was using a torch. "A torch produces no fumes or toxic emissions. It makes no noise. The same would apply to battery powered trains, but only they'd be bigger than torches", he told us yesterday.

FREE RANGE

Craven is convinced that the main advantage of his scheme is the enormous economy involved. "Converting to battery power will not require enormous investment, because we can simply adapt existing trains to run on batteries", he explained. And junior newshound John has even prepared detailed plans to show how batteries could be fitted to BR's existing trains. "If a 6 inch long torch uses 4 inch long batteries, then a 90 foot long train will require a 60 foot long battery", he told us.

PERCHERY

But Craven admitted that there may yet be technical problems to overcome before Britain's railways were running smoothly on batteries. "The problem with batteries is that if they go flat and you don't take them out, sticky stuff comes out of the top, and that could ruin trains", he told us.

OVEN READY

A spokesman for British Rail told us that they were currently evaluating several ideas submitted to them by seventies children's TV presenters, including a 'Wind Powered' train designed by Tony Hart, but said that it may be several months before the results of their investigations are known.

So says Newsround newshound John

Telly's bright spark John (above) campaigns for battery trains

Butty drought hits Britain

Sandwich stocks throughout Britain yesterday hit an all-time low, with empty shelves beginning to appear in sandwich shops across the country. And there are fears of worse to come, as the country plunges into the worst sandwich drought in living memory.

Many sandwich shops were closing their doors yesterday as supplies ran out, and disappointed lunchtime shoppers were returning to work empty handed. And larger retailers reported queues of shoppers snapping up remaining stocks.

BRANCH

At Marks & Spencer's Bayswater road branch there were reports of large queues, and only a few salmon, celery and cucumber sandwiches remained by lunchtime.

TRUNK

Mr Ted Formby, who has sold sandwiches at his restaurant in Sheffield's Meadow Hall shopping centre for over 3 years, says he's never seen anything like it. "We're right out of sandwiches", he told us. "I've had to turn people away".

TWIGS

The good news for sandwich buyers is that the shortage looks set to end. "There is no shortage of bread or sandwich fillings, and so we'd expect to see fresh sandwiches in the shops within the next two to three days", said Trevor Phillipson, spokeman for the Confederation of British Sandwich Manufacturers and Retailers.

MAKE bathtime as much fun for kiddies as a visit to the seaside by pouring a bucket of sand, a bag of salt, and a dog turd into the bath.
Archie Hitch
Merton

MOTORISTS. Stick a small photograph of a friend or relative to the top, right hand corner of your roof lining, and talk to it earnestly when alone in the car. Other drivers will be convinced you own a 'hands free' car phone.
M. B. Best
Reading

RAMBLERS. In the country, leaving gates open will help the farmer out as he will not have to climb down from his tractor.
W. A. Pratt
London

GIVE your bird box a 'thatched cottage' look by fixing two Shredded Wheat to the roof.
A. E. Greenall
Liverpool L11

SAVE wear and tear on door hinges by only opening doors a little bit, and then squeezing through the gap.
Dino
Eastleigh

WOOD STAIN is a fast and attractive alternative to sunbed treatments.
Mr T. Eebly
Wanstead

SMEAR cheap purple dye in your armpits to make people think you've been wearing one of those fantastic, expensive T shirts that change colour with your body temperature.
Mark Roulston
Swansea

CYCLISTS. Why not try stopping at red lights like everyone else instead of riding up onto the pavement to avoid them. Stupid bastards.
M. Burridge
Newcastle

MAKE your toast into the shape of a Maltese Cross simply and effectively by nibbling out a section from each of the four corners.
J. Hudson
Mitcham

NOW IT'S THE QUEEN MUM AND FRANK BOUGH!

A new Royal sex scandal is set to rock the foundations of the already shaky House of Windsor. And sensationally, it's the *Queen Mum* who's been caught at it this time — with TV drugs sex fetish star Frank Bough!

A saucy car phone conversation between the wrinkly Royal and randy Frank was accidentally picked up on a hair dryer being used by housewife Vera Gubbins, 42, who lives just 270 miles from Windsor Castle.

HAIR

Vera, from Thornaby, near Middlesbrough, couldn't believe her ears as she sat drying her hair. Suddenly voices began to come out of her 15-year-old hair dryer.

OH CALCUTTA!

"I immediately recognised Frank Bough's voice as I've seen him on the telly. Then suddenly I realised he was talking to the Queen Mother. She kept refering to the Blitz, and horse racing, and she asked him to get her a bottle of gin on his way home. Bough always referred to her as 'Fishbones', and the conversation got quite fruity at times."

GODSPELL

Quick thinking Mrs Gubbins switched on her husband's telephone answering machine and pointed the hair dryer at it, and luckily the entire conversation was recorded onto a cassette.

We were offered a copy of the cassette by Mrs Gubbins' husband Charlie, plus colour photographs of Frank Bough and the Queen Mother frolicking by a swimming pool, for £2,000. In order to respect the privacy of the Queen Mother we refused to publish either.

EVITA

However, if you'd like to hear the tape and see the pictures, we'll lend you them, for £100. Just send an envelope containing £250 cash (£100 plus a £150 deposit) plus a stamped addressed return envelope. We'll then send you the tape and pictures. When you're finished with them, send them back and we'll return your deposit. Honest.

RYVITA

Send your cash to 'Queen Mumgate Tape (and pictures)', Viz, P.O. Box 1PT, Newcastle upon Tyne, NE99 1PT. Please note it may take several years before you get the tape and pictures. But be patient, it will be your turn eventually. Proceeds from our 'Queen Mumgate tape (and pictures)' scandal will all go to charity.

Spanky Frankie's 'phone call to 'Fishbones'

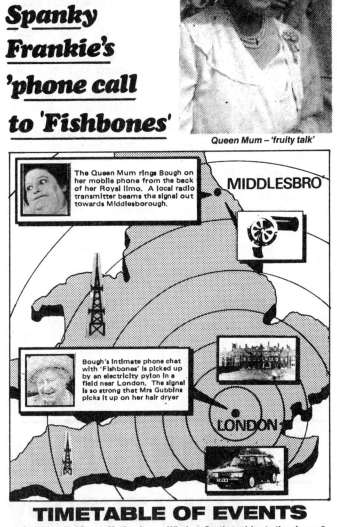

Queen Mum – 'fruity talk'

The Queen Mum rings Bough on her mobile phone from the back of her Royal limo. A local radio transmitter beams the signal out towards Middlesborough.

MIDDLESBRO

Bough's intimate phone chat with 'Fishbones' is picked up by an electricity pylon in a field near London. The signal is so strong that Mrs Gubbins picks it up on her hair dryer.

LONDON

TIMETABLE OF EVENTS

1. At 8.45am the Queen Mother leaves Windsor Castle to drive to the shops. 2. 8.50am Vera Gubbins washes her hair 270 miles away in Thornaby. 3. 9.10am The Queen Mother makes a call to Frank Bough on her car phone. 4. 9.12am Vera Gubbins picks up call on her hair dryer and records it on her telephone answering machine. 5. 9.15am she rings the newspapers. 6. 9.30am we pay her £2000. 7. 11.45am Mrs Gubbins has spent the lot.

LISTEN IN AND WIN!

We're offering a hair dryer, a telephone answering machine and 12 cans of lager to the reader who sends us the best Royal telephone conversation recording.

FRIDGE

You can pick up Royal telephone conversations on most types of electrical equipment around the house – transistor radios, fridge freezers, microwaves, tumble dryers etc.

Simply make your own recording of a private Royal telephone conversation – whether it's Fergie on your food mixer, or Di on your dish washer – and send it to us.

SNOOKER TABLE

Send them to 'Rec_____al', Viz, P.O. _____ Newcastle _____, NE99 1PT.

COMPETITION CLOSED

83

ON THE JOB!

Britain may be down in the Euro-dumps as far as our economy is concerned — but there's still one thing that we are best at.

A recent survey shows that we come top of the table for *office hanky panky*.

SIZZLING

The sizzling survey compared the sexual habits of office workers throughout the EEC. And the results show clearly that when it comes to *bonking the boss* the British are best!

STAGGERING

A staggering *12 per cent* of office workers in Britain admit to having an affair with one or more of their colleagues, compared to only 11 per cent in France, and a measly 10 per cent of dismal Deutchlanders!

SAUCY

And fortunate female office workers in Britain are *three times* more likely to be sexually harassed by saucy senior male colleagues than their European counterparts.

And if any more evidence was needed to prove that Britain's office workers are the sexiest in Europe, the incidence of rape in the workplace is a sizzling 7 per cent higher in the UK than in other countries. A statistic that even the steamy Swedes, amorous French and randy Italians cannot match.

BONKING

Yes, Britain is *officially* office bonking bonkers, so we've organised our own survey to find out just how many of you office workers out there are *at it*, and exactly *what*, *where* and *how* you are getting up to!

KNOCK UP

Just fill in this fun questionnaire and send it to us. We'll analyse the results in full, knock up a few graphs, pie charts etc., and publish them together with numerous pictures of female

You don't have to be SEX mad to work here, but it helps

models posing provocatively around filing cabinets in their underwear. *It's Britain's biggest ever Sex At Work Survey*, and we want *everyone* to take part.

Photocopy your tits and win a prize

And if you're a saucy secretary, you could pick up one of our fabulous *booby prizes* by enclosing a

photocopy of your tits with your completed questionnaire. We'll be awarding a terrific three draw filing cabinet (complete with suspension files) for the best colour copy tits we receive and a super swivel typist's chair for the best black and white knockers.

BREASTS

Simply complete the questionnaire by placing ticks in the appropriate boxes, and send it to: Viz Office Sex Survey (& Tit Photocopy Competition), P.O. Box 1PT, Newcastle upon Tyne, NE99 1PT. (Photocopies of breasts must be same size, on *A3* paper. No A4 knockers please).

ELEPHANTS' EARS – NEW THEORY

A former England international footballer is about to rewrite the wildlife record books.

Ace goalscorer turned keen amateur zoologist Frank Worthington believes he has made an amazing discovery which turns accepted zoological theories about elephants upside down. For former Leicester City centre forward Frank claims the experts have got it wrong – and Indian elephants have in fact got *bigger* ears than African elephants, not the other way round.

ELEPHANT

For years schoolchildren have been taught that the African elephant – larger than its relative the Indian elephant – has got the biggest ears. But now, thanks to Frank, the natural history books may have to be rewritten.

"I couldn't believe it at first", said Frank, always a favourite with the football fans. "I was just looking through a book when I suddenly realised the ears on an Indian elephant are bigger than the ears on an African elephant", he told us.
Frank has submitted his findings to the British Natural History Museum.

Once a deadly football marksman, Frank now seems set to carve out an equally exciting career as a zoologist.
Footnote: Frank Worthington last night withdrew his claim that Indian elephants have bigger ears than African elephants. "It was all a big mix up", he told us. "I was looking at the wrong picture in my book".

OFFICE SEX SURVEY

Tick whichever box applies

Have you ever had sex with a collegue at work? ☐ yes ☐ no

If so, where did you do it?
☐ Behind the filing cabinet
☐ In the stockroom
☐ On the photocopier

How many times did you do it? ☐ 1-5 ☐ 5-10 ☐ 10-15

MALLET HAMMERS NAIL

TV celebrity turned pop star Timmy Mallet yesterday hit out at the new album by actor turned singer Jimmy Nail.

SCOUSE

"I haven't heard it yet, but a friend of mine has, and they didn't like it', he told us. Meanwhile 'Giz a job' star Jimmy, who shot to fame as scouse TV detective Taggart, was unavailable for comment.

We've gone CONKERS BONKERS!

If there's one thing in Britain today that won't be hit by the recession, it's conkers. For while house prices plumit, the pound tumbles and businesses go to the wall, kids are collecting conkers as enthusiastically as ever.

And we're getting into the *swing* by going horse chest-*nutty!* Yes, we're inviting everyone in Britain to forget their troubles, and play conkers instead.

CONKERS

All you have to do to enter our Conker Competition is go out and find a conker. You'll find them lying on the ground under Horse Chestnut trees. When you think you've got a good one, drill a hole in it, and thread some string through, then knot it at both ends. Then post your conker to us, and we will enter it into our Conker Challenge.

CHEATING

Your conker will take part in a special match against our own Champion Conker. It will be a fair fight, with no cheating, and will be witnessed by us. If your conker wins, we will send you a £100 sweet voucher valid at any sweet shop, plus 100

It's Britain's biggest conker competition

marbles. All conkers will be returned together with a certificate.

STRING

So come on, collect those conkers and send them as soon as you can. The competition closed about 2 years ago. Send your conker on a string, plus a 50p entry fee and a stamped addressed return envelope, to: Viz Conkers Bonkers Horse Chest*nutty* Conker Competition, P.O. Box 1PT, Newcastle upon Tyne, NE99 1PT.

Please note: Any conkers which have been soaked in vinegar, cooked in an oven or otherwise tampered with, will be disqualified. The judges decision is final.

Conker campaigner David Alton yesterday

Play it safe says MP Dave

A word of warning to conker collectors from Conker Safety Campaigner MP David Alton.

DANGER

"I would ask anyone going out to collect conkers to take my advice and follow the Conker Code. Conkering can be great fun if you avoid danger by following these simple tips", said David.

• Collect conkers from the ground around trees. Don't throw sticks or stones to dislodge them from the tree. "Throwing things is dangerous, and can damage the tree", said Mr Alton, MP for Liverpool Mossley Hill.

• Never climb a tree to reach conkers. Falling can cause serious injuries.

• Don't trespass to reach conker trees. Collect conkers in public parks, etc. *Not* in people's gardens.

• Finally, stay away from busy roads. Collecting conkers on or near a busy road simply isn't worth the risk.

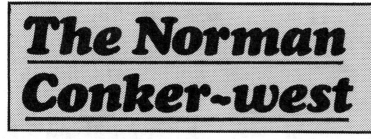

The Norman Conker-west

We asked a few famous faces whether they'd be entering Britain's biggest Conker Competition.

Chancellor Norman Lamont forgot his economic worries for a few moments and said he'd love to take part, providing he could get hold of a decent conker. "It's been some time since I went out looking for conkers, and I doubt if I'm as agile as I used to be. I certainly won't be climbing any trees", quipped the Government's money expert.

SEX

Judith Mellor, long suffering wife of sex scandal 'Minister for Fun' hubby David, said she'd never played conkers.

GIRL

"I was a girl when I was younger, and it was more the boys that did that sort of thing".

CARROT

Welsh comic Jasper Carrott told us he wouldn't have time to collect conkers this year.

PEAS

"I'll be too busy writing new material for my hilarious TV show, and recording a follow up to my hit single 'Funky Moped'", he told us.

Mellor - was girl

Carrot - hilarious

DAFT BUGGER

OH NO. I THINK I'VE LOCKED MY KEYS IN THE CAR AGAIN.

'I STILL USE PUBLIC LAVATORIES'

Millionaire game show king Jim Bowen may have made his fortune as host of the highly popular darts show 'Bullseye' — but he's still prepared to use public lavatories.

Says Bullseye's T.V. comic Jim

Comic Jim, who's showbiz career began with appearances on TV's The Comedians, has climbed to the pinnacle of the entertainment ladder. And the one time schoolteacher now drives a glittering Rolls-Royce and wears £40 shoes when he's not swimming in the luxurious heated pool at his sumptuous Lancashire home.

LAVATORIES

Yet Jim, 62, still has his feet firmly on the ground, and is, under certain circumstances, still prepared to use public lavatories.

LAVATORY

"My wife and I often go shopping – we've worked for our money and we're not afraid to spend it. On one occasion I needed to use the lavatory while we were shopping. I didn't think twice about using the public loo nearby".

LAVATORY

But that's typical of Jim, 65, who has very much steered his own course throughout a spectacularly successful showbiz career.

TV stardom has meant many changes for Jim. Now the proud owner of an old motorbike, he is not ashamed of his wealth. "I've worked hard for my money, and I'm not afraid to spend it', he told us. And yet, at 66, Rolls-Royce and £40 shoe owning former school-teacher Jim, 59, is still prepared to use a public lavatory.

LUXURY

Taking a break from his meteoric showbiz career to sip champagne by his luxury pool, Jim kicks off his £40 shoes. But even as he dips a toe into his luxury water, Jim's feet remain firmly on the ground, "I wouldn't think twice about using a public lavatory," he told us.

Luxury lifestyle - Home for millionaire Jim is a lavish former railway station.

FISH HOOKED ON ROD

Singer Fish out of Marillion is crazy about fellow Scot Rod Stewart. And the strapping six footer is even a member of Rod's fan club.

FISH

"I've got all his records, and I think he's great", said Fish yesterday.

BIRDS

Meanwhile, raunchy Rod, who likes to shag the birds and play football, was unavailable for comment.

89

20 THINGS YOU NEVER KNEW ABOUT MARZIPAN

It's in cakes and it's on cake ingredient shelves in the local supermarket. Yes, there's no getting away from marzipan. It's the cake ingredient that everyone wants to have on their cake and eat it. But how much do we really know about marzipan? We picked away the icing to reveal twenty fascinating facts about Britain's favourite cake covering.

1. You have to be *nuts* to make marzipan. That's because nuts – almonds to be precise – are what marzipan is made out of.

2. The name marzipan derives from latin – literally meaning 'bread of mars'. That's because the Roman astronomers believed the pasty cake covering originated from the red planet.

3. Marzipan first came to Britain in the 15th century when merchants returning from China used it to pack boxes of fragile china plates, cups and saucers.

4. To this day the idea of eating marzipan is unthinkable in China where it remains the country's main packing material.

5. Ironically, Chinese chefs use polystyrene, which they consider a delicacy, to coat their Christmas cakes.

6. Followers of a little known religion – Marzipology – refuse to eat marzipan. They believe that owing to a typographical error in the Bible marzipan was omitted from the gifts delivered to Jesus by the three wise men, and the word 'myrhh' was incorrectly used in it's place. They believe that marzipan is Holy, and they light special marzipan candles in their churches.

Remember the *true* meaning of Christmas...

NUTS

The Nuts of Great Britain and Wales. For further information dial 100 and ask for Freephone Nuts.

7. Stars who enjoy marzipan include controversial slap head Sinead O'Connor, Catherine Zeta Jones out of the Darling Buds of May, and Eric Clapton.

Marzipan fan Darling Catherine Zeta Jones

8. Meanwhile, American rocker Bruce Springsteen hates the stuff. He shocked guests at an MTV awards party recently by removing marzipan from his cake and leaving it on the side of his plate.

Stars who have not yet publicly expressed an opinion on marzipan include cockney comic and Eastenders star Mike Reid, actress Julia Sawalha and TV funny man Jasper Carrott.

10. Last Christmas Britain's housewives spent an average of £78 stocking up on marzipan for use as a cake covering and decoration. That's more than we spent on candles, miniature plastic Santa Claus and Christmas tree figures, candle holders and little silver edible balls put together.

11. Marzipan can be made at home using icing sugar, caster sugar, almonds, eggs, vanilla essence and lemon juice.

12. Dentists prefer to make their own marzipan as opposed to buying it in the shops. That's because ready mixed marzipan contains up to 50 per cent more sugar than the home-made variety.

13. Pop star Marc Almond changed his name from Robert Marzipan Blenkinsop. He thought Almond would be less of a mouthful.

14. If you were caught with marzipan in France during the last war, you'd have been shot by the Nazis. For marzipan is identical in texture and appearance to gelignite, and the French resistance used Christmas cakes as a means of smuggling explosives.

15. Millionaire rock star Mick Jagger is mad about marzipan. Indeed he chose his home – Mustique in the Carribean – because it is the world's second largest marzipan producing country.

Marzipan man Jagger

16. America is the largest, with an annual output of 140 million tons – enough marzipan, if it were rolled into a thin strip, to stretch to the moon and back – ten times! All 140 million tons are exported to Belgium.

17. Russian marzipan contains no sugar or almonds. Intead it is made of sand and lime. 'Ugstondk', as it's known, is used extensively in the building industry.

18. Top of the Pops dancers Pan's People were originally called Marzipan's People after the seventies teenage craze of eating marzipan. Kids used marzi-pan to give them extra energy in much the same way that Ecstasy is used today. However, the name was changed as the BBC felt the word 'marzipan' was too controversial.

19. There was 'marzipan-dimonium' in Hollywood recently when pint-sized Batman star Danny Devito opened Hollywood's first marzipan restaurant. Top stars queued for hours to choose from 150 different flavours of marzipan on offer. Demand was so great that the restaurant completely sold out of marzipan within half an hour.

20. Marzipan hasn't always been used to decorate cakes. During the war hair combs and brushes were rationed, and soldiers would use a strip of pink marzipan in their hair as a false parting.

A DIFFERENT KIND OF LOVE

93

Filmed at THE MELBOURNE DINER (above Riverside), Melbourne Street, Newcastle.
Wide selection of vegetarian and non vegetarian food, beers, wines, sandwiches. Bits of cake etc.

95

Photography by Colin D.   CD 7.92   viz 55

Faddy eaters!

TV tough guys the Gladiators are fussy about their food. That's the shock news that's set to rock Britain's favourite TV show.

The Gladiators has taken the TV world by storm. But what audiences don't realise is that superheroes like Wolf, Panther and Flame are in fact *choosey eaters.*

CANTEEN

That's the dramatic claim being made by former TV canteen assistant Ethel Brownbridge. And shey says that staff at the BBC canteen where she worked for three months became so fed up with the muscle-bound Gladiators picking at their food they **BANNED** them eating there.

REFRECTORY

She claims that the super fit Gladiators were
• **FINICKY** about what they ate
• **DIFFICULT** to please with an amazing list of likes and dislikes, and
• **FUSSY** about little things, like peas going cold.

CAFE

"Wolf was the worst", Ethel told us. "He'd always ask for a children's portion, and he had to have a glass of warm milk with it. He even made me mash up his fish fingers on one occasion to prove that there were no bones in them."

BEEF CAKE

Warrior was just as bad. He looked like a real beef cake, so I used to give him extra servings of vegetables. But he never ate his peas because he said they were cold, and he used to leave his chips too because he only ate crinkle cut ones".

MEATLOAF

The female stars of the hit show were just as bad, Ethel recalls. "Flame wouldn't eat anything for a week. Eventually we rang her mum. She explained that Flame only ate out of a special 'Winnie the Pooh' bowl – so from then on she brought that in with her and she was fine".

Tempers would often flare if the Gladiators didn't get their way.

OZZY OSBORNE

"One day Saracen was sulking in the corner. He said he wasn't eating his rice pudding because it had skin on the top. I told him that he wasn't leaving the canteen until he'd ate it all.

SMASHED

Next thing I knew he flew into a rage. He smashed his hand down onto the table sending the rice pudding flying in the air. There was rice everywhere.

FRUIT

On another occasion Lightening came in. She was very fussy, and always refused to eat fruit. Well, she'd just finished a salad, when Panther told her that tomatoes are a fruit, and she'd just eaten one.

SMELL

Suddenly she kicked the table over and began screaming. She screamed till she was blue in the face, then she was sick, and out came the tomato. I asked Wolf to help me clean it up, but he said the smell of tomatoes made him faint.

Queues would often form in the canteen while we faffed on with the Gladiators' food. Once, I remember Panther had ordered baked beans on toast. As usual I was cleaning the tomato sauce off her beans using boiling water and a sieve. When I'd eventually finished she took one look at the plate and hurled it through a window.

SIGHT

Eventually when we calmed her down she explained that the toast had been soggy, and the crusts hadn't been cut off".

TOUCH

Eventually, TV bosses banned the Gladiators from the canteen after complaints from other customers, among them Noel Edmonds.

TASTE

"Noel had been sitting on a table next to the Gladiators when Saracen complained that he was eating too loudly and it was putting him off his food. There was a brief argument following which Saracen leapt onto the table and battered Edmonds about the head with his pugil stick. Noel looked pretty badly shaken".

Trouble appeared to have followed the Gladiators when they visited a McDonald's fast food restaurant near the TV studios a few days later. Police were called after £2000 worth of damage was done to fixtures and fittings following a dispute over mustard on a cheese burger ordered by one of the stars.

Next week: How Wolf dries his bottom with a hand towel. We expose the disguisting and unhygienic toilet habits of the TV Gladiators!

The Gladiators (clockwise, right to left) Flame, Jaguar, Panther, Daimler, Orion, Conservatory, Trousers and Hose pipe.

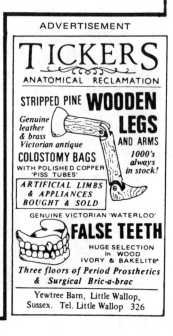

By the
way…

TWINKLE TWINKLE LI

Not many people can claim to have frolicked with a nude Madonna, had a bath with Burt Reynolds, and changed Elvis Presley's nappy — all in one week!

But Enid Parsons can. And she could also tell you about the time she smacked Mick Jagger's bottom. Because Enid, or "Auntie Enid" as the stars have come to know her, is the world's number one celebrity babysitter.

SIZZLING

But now, aged 62, Enid plans to quit the celebrity babysitting game, and plans to reveal the bedroom secrets of the baby stars in a sizzling new book soon to be published. And here, in an exclusive extract, Enid lets us in on just a few of the thrills and the spills she had as a babysitter to the stars.

❝Babysitting the stars isn't as glamourous as it may sound. If you've seen one dirty nappy, you've seen 'em all. It doesn't matter whether it's Elvis Presley's or Marilyn Monroe's. They all smell the same.

NEIGHBOURS

My first celebrity babysitting job came about when our neighbours asked if I'd look after their son one evening. Their name was Mr and Mrs Richard, and I'd often seen their son Cliff playing in the garden. Even then, at the age of 3, he was a talented young man. He sang me songs all evening, and told me how he was going to be a pop star, then become Christian later on. Of course I just laughed.

Cliff – became Christian later

But now Cliff is the one who's laughing. His dreams have all come true. I'm pleased for him, but a little sad also. Sad that he never married. I changed young Cliff's nappy a thousand times, and I'll tell you what – if the girls knew what he had in his pants, he wouldn't be a *Bachelor boy* for long!

Little Mick had nowt in his nappy

Of course in my line of work I saw all the stars in the nude. I was bathing Mick Jagger before he was old enough to *eat* a Mars bar, never mind do anything else with it. He may have big lips, but when I last saw young Mick in the altogether he had nothing to shout about in the trouser department.

Britain's No. 1 Celebrity babysitter reveals all!

The hardest part of babysitting the stars is actually getting the little rascals into bed. Like normal kids, they always want to stay up and play. With one notable exception.

HOME & WAY

Getting young Rod Stewart into bed was always plain *Sailing* for me. Rod must have been about 6 when I looked after him. He looked a picture in a little tartan kilt his mother had knitted, and shiny red shoes. I remember sitting watching Thomas The Tank Engine videos with him after tea, and half way through he'd always ask if he could go to bed.

THE SULLIVANS

He'd put himself to bed early every night, and I'd never hear a squeak out of him. Then one day I decided to pop upstairs and check on him. I couldn't believe my eyes when I opened his bedroom door.

THE YOUNG DOCTORS

There was Rod, romping naked in his cot with 6 busty Swedish models!

SKIPPY

Needless to say I threw the models out of the house and smacked Rod's bottom for being so naughty. Despite all his fame and fortune, and the beautiful women he has had since, that's one night I bet he'll never forget.

Raunchy Rod – early sex romp

You'd be surprised how many toddlers have sex on their minds. A little boy called Robin Askwith was the worst. One day his parents went out for a meal with their neighbours, a Mr and Mrs Geeson from next door, so I was left to look after young Robin and their daughter Judy too. That evening Robin asked if they could go out and play in my car. It seemed like a harmless enough idea. After all, there's not much two 3-year-olds can get up to. At least that's what I thought.

FLIPPER

The next thing I know the horn was beeping, the windscreen wipers were going at a hundred miles an hour, and the whole car started to bounce up and down. The windows were all misted up, and there were loud 'springy' noises coming from inside. Suddenly the bonnet sprung up, the wheels and doors fell off, and the cap popped off the radiator and steam billowed out.

RIN TIN TIN

Needless to say rascal Robin was sent to bed early, with no tea, and a very sore bottom. Nowadays smacking children is frowned upon by many folks. But in my experience it does then no harm – perhaps with one exception.

I KNOW I SAID I WAS GOING OUT TONIGHT, BUT SOMETHING'S COME UP AT WORK AND I CAN'T.

THAT'S A SHAME.

I DUNNO. IT DOES YOU GOOD TO LET YOUR HARE DOWN NOW AND AGAIN.

TLE STARS

Bough – spank obsession

McEnroe – 'Superbrat'

Young Frank Bough was one of my first charges. Mr and Mrs Bough used to go to the cinema on Fridays and asked me to look after little Frank. Occasionally, if he was naughty, I'd give him a smack.

BLACK BEAUTY

Gradually his behaviour worsened, and the spankings increased. Soon I realised he was deliberately being naughty in order to get spanked. And the more I smacked him, the more excited he became. On one occasion he suggested I use a leather belt with studs on it instead of my usual slipper. I should have realised what was happening. He was obviously developing an obsession, and I feel somehow responsible for the problems he is suffering now.

FOLLYFOOT

Of course little Frank was an exception. In my view some of the stars of today could still do with a good smacking. Take John McEnroe for example. I used to get paid a pound a night extra for going to America to look after little Johnny. Mind you, he was a bad lad then, always arguing about his bedtime, and using filthy language. But I didn't take any nonsense – I put him straight over my knee and gave him six of the best.

CATWEAZLE

Nowadays when I see him at Wimbledon, shouting and swearing, I know what the umpires should do. They should slap him firmly across the back of the legs, and tell him that if he doesn't behave himself, he'll be put straight to bed. And if he swears, they should wash his mouth out with carbolic soap.

Great Train Robbers were 'little angels'

You never know what kids will turn out like when they're older. For example, I once babysat the Great Train Robbers, when they were 7. They were little Angels, no trouble at all. In fact I even dropped a pound coin down the back of their settee while I was watching telly, and they were so honest, they handed it back to me.

MICK McMANUS

However, the opposite was true of Jeffrey Archer. I only ever looked after him once, but he insisted that I read him bedtime stories – until 4 in the morning! I didn't realise until later that he'd been copying the stories down in an old exercise book which he had under the bedsheets. And he'd written his own name on the front."

KID CHOCOLATE

Next week: How my car ended up being lowered into a swimming pool by a giant crane the night I babysat a young boy by the name of Jeremy Beadle, etc. etc.

Here's a fun competition for you to enter. Auntie Enid has given us photos she took of some of today's top stars whilst they were babies. And all you have to do is look at the snaps and identify the star.

BABIES

To make it easier for you we've given a little clue for each. If you think you recognise the stars, pop their names on a postcard and send it to us. There's a super space rocket holiday for 2 on Mars for the lucky winner, and £2000 worth of pianos for three runners up. And some lace curtains.

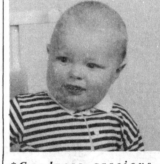

Goodness gracious, guys'n'gals. 'Ow's about this then for a bonny baby? Euu-eurgh-eurgh!

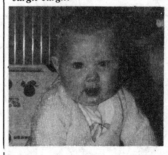

Nice to see this baby, to see this baby … nice! But those lovely curls are hair today, gone tomorrow…

Tie me kangaroo down, sport. Didgeri-do you recognise this bearded Aussie singing cartoonist? Can you see who it is yet?

BATTLE OF THE BANDS

A major 'Battle of the Bands' looked set to erupt last night between two warring rock groups. But rather than a musical contest, this dispute looks like ending in fisticuffs.

METAL

Veteran TV presenter Cliff Michelmore, who quit BBC's Wish You Were Here programme to form Death Metal outfit *Cliff Michelmore's Thunderflash* is claiming that rock rival Robert Robinson has stolen songs written by him whilst he was working at the BBC.

Robinson took his own band *Battleaxe* on the road shortly after retiring as host of BBC2's Call My Bluff. But furious Michelmore, who's five piece Thunderflash recently sold out a twenty date European tour, claims the former Ask The Family host has recorded three songs belonging to him on his new Battleaxe album.

SHIT

Yesterday Robinson seemed unrepentant. "That guy Michelmore is just a giant shit, and if his band are anything like as bad as him, they're just wasting their f***ing time".

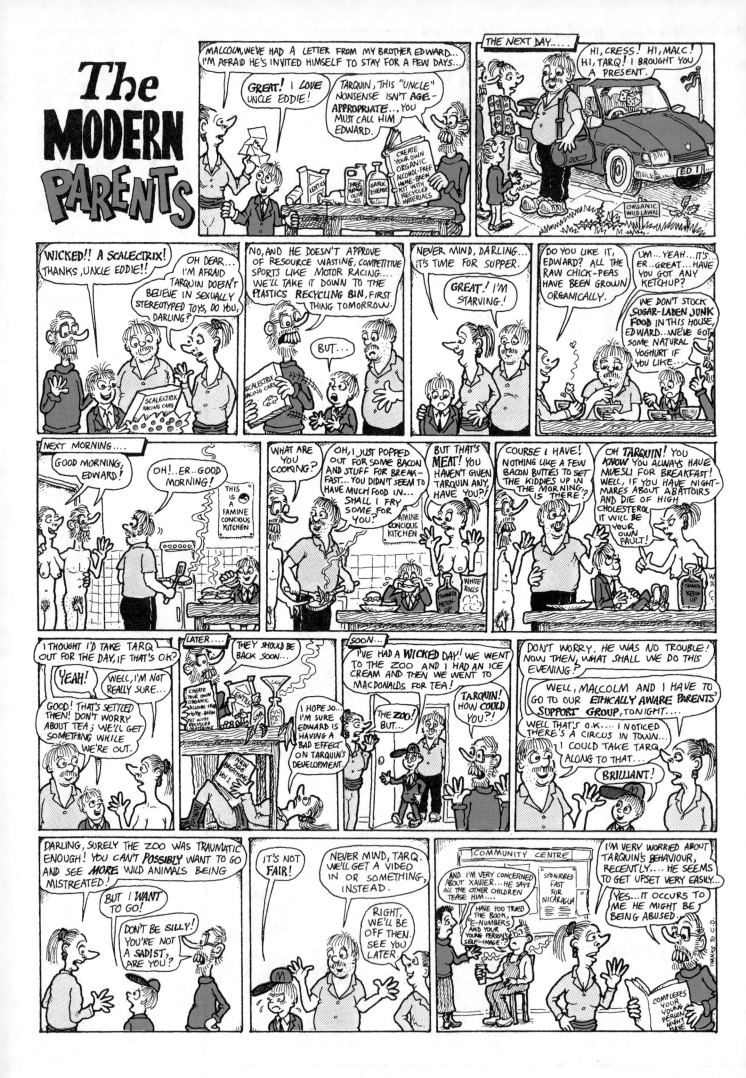

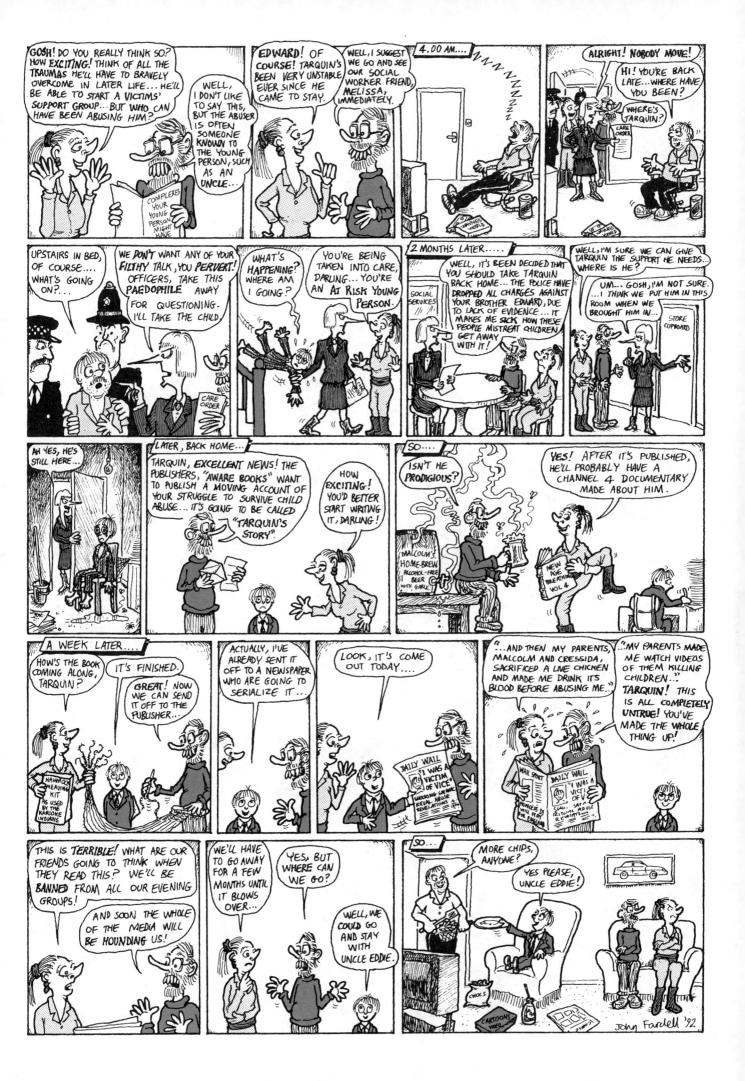

ROCK AGAINST DINOSAURS

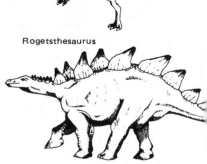

Fellow Geordies Sting and Jimmy Nail have joined forces in an unlikely battle — against dinosaurs.

For the Tyneside singing and acting duo share a common fear that dinosaurs could reappear on Earth. And they hope that by acting now they can prevent the giant creatures from conquering the planet.

By our Showbiz Staff

DINOSAURS

Jimmy Nail, alias TV tough guy cop Spender – admits that the idea was his. Jimmy has suffered from dinosophobia – the fear of dinosaurs – since early childhood.

COPING SAWS

"There's just something about dinosaurs that terrifies me", Jim confided. "As a child I was scared to go out of the house in case there were dinosaurs in the street. It was a really serious problem".

COLD SORES

On one occasion young Jimmy stayed in bed for three weeks. "I was convinced there was a dinosaur under my bed. I thought if I put my foot on the floor it would bite it off". Jimmy eventually clambered onto a wardrobe and escaped to the kitchen where his mother was less than sympathetic. "I got a right bashing", says Jim.

HERPES

"Even then I didn't realise how serious a problem it was. It's only now, when I've started to talk about it to other people, that I've begun to realise how much it has affected me".

HIS CHIPS

Jimmy was delighted when he read that fellow Geordie Sting also suffered from anxieties concerning dinosaurs, and he immediately got in touch. Now the chart topping double act are working together to overcome their

Nail – scared of dinosaurs

Sting – also scared of dinosaurs

fear of the giant reptiles, and they hope to enlist the help of other rock stars, actors and Northern celebrities.

LINDISFARNE

"We've had a great response so far", Jimmy told us. "Brendan Foster and Steve Cram have both offered to help, and Lindisfarne will be playing a benefit concert to raise runds for us in the near future. Jimmy hopes to set up a registered charity N.E.S.A.D. – North East Stars Against Dinosaurs – to help channel funds to where they are most needed and help fellow celebrities overcome their dinosaur anxieties.

Geordies join forces to battle prehistoric menace

Nail's nightmare

Here's Jimmy Nail's six most frightening dinosaurs.

Triceratops – a powerful, thick set, relatively small dinosaur with distinctive horns. "My worst nightmare is being trapped in a small space – like my bedroom – by one of these. They're so strong, yet manoeuvrable", says Jimmy.

Tyranosaurus – the largest meat eater ever to stalk the Earth. "It's the sheer power of this one that frightens me. It can actually run faster than an average saloon car, and bullets would bounce off it".

Stegosaurus – This North American dinosaur of the Jurassic period had distinctive boney plates along its spine. "It's those horrible sharp spikes on its back that worry me most", says Jim.

Plesiosaurus – a giant water lizard of the early Cretaceous period. "It sounds silly, but when I first met my wife I wouldn't get in a bath in case one of these came up the plughole. She has helped me to overcome that fear, but I would never swim in the sea".

Tyranosaurus rex

Rogetsthesaurus

Rhamphorhynchus – a giant flying pterosaur descended from tree-living lizards. "With it's leathery wings and razor sharp beak I am terrified that one day one of these could swoop out of the sky and eat me", says Jimmy.

Deinonychus – a small carnivorous dinosaur which hunted in packs. "The thought of being attacked and pulled to the ground by a pack of these is never far from my mind".

Celebrity scares!

Jimmy Nail is by no means the first showbusiness celebrity to reveal a secret phobia. *Celebrity phobias* – irrational fears suffered by the stars of show business – have been around as long as show business itself.

In the thirties Lancashire born **George Formby** dropped a bombshell when he revealed to stunned cinema audiences that he was afraid of shiny things. Movie makers went to great lengths to ensure that mirrors, polished surfaces, ball bearings and silverware were removed from film sets before Formby arrived.

Formby – leant on lampost

GEORDIE

Of today's celebrities **Geoff Capes** possibly boasts the most unusual phobia – a fear of budgies. Unlike many stars who try to hide their fears, former policeman Geoff has tackled his problem head on. Strong man Geoff decided to overcome his phobia by breeding budgies in the back yard of his home. And it worked. For Geoff, once a prisoner in his own home, now comes and goes freely, and isn't afraid of budgies anymore.

GOLDIE

Seventies pop idol **Gilbert O'Sullivan's** career was cut short – by a fear of anal germs. Obsessed with bottom hygiene, O'Sullivan would spend hours before and after gigs steeping his bum in a bath of Sterident. And the obsessive star would even book himself into a private clinic for expensive anal detoxification programmes every time he farted. Eventually his record sales began to fall as he spent more time in the bathroom and less in the recording studio.

Blessed – shouty crackers

Shouty crackers actor **Brian Blessed's** star phobia cost him his first major acting role. Brian was offered the part of TV's Captain Birdseye, but during rehearsals for a 30 second TV ad he began to sweat and suffered a panic attack. Top showbusiness doctors later diagnosed Brian as suffering from orpainophobia – an irrational fear of any frozen food coated in golden breadcrumbs. Blessed lost the job, and has since avoided all contact with fish fingers, Crispy Pancakes, scampi, Mini Kievs and Chicksticks.

FRANK GETS THE HUMP OVER CAMELS

Former soccer ace Frank Worthington is today puzzled about camels.

Worthington, the dashing goal hero who scored with his feet *and* with the ladies during the seventies, has swapped his football boots for books – about camels! But despite reading up on his favourite animal, Frank admits to being somewhat baffled by their humps.

Worthington – camel headache

HUMPED

In his soon to be published autobiography, the former England international admits he can't tell the difference between a dromedary and a bachtrian camel – the one and two humped varieties.

"For some reason throughout my career I've never been able to remember which has one hump and which has two. To this day I'm still unsure", admits Frank in his book, due for publication in the new year.

POKED

We rang Jersey zoo keeper and animal book writer Gerald Durrell and asked if he had any hints for Frank.

"There is a simple way to remember which is which", said Gerald. "The letter 'D' for dromedary, when laid on its back, resembles a single hump. The letter 'B' for bachtrian similarly resembles two humps. It's easy."

KNOBBED

When we asked Mr Durrell how many humps the camels in his zoo have got he didn't hear us, because he'd already hung up.

I WAS BENNY HILL'S LOVER

Says Queen's Freddie's sex change dad

A man who fathered the late Freddie Mercury has revealed himself as a saucy sex change cheat.

For he admits that during a brief period working as a sexy glamour showgirl he bedded tubby comic Benny Hill.

Frank Hobson, 42, rocked the showbiz world with his stunning revelation that he was father of tragic AIDS victim Freddie.

CAREER

Although he never met his son, Frank followed his pop career closely. "I used to watch him on Top Of The Pops every week. And I went to see him play live once – at Live Aid in 1986. I stood at the back so he wouldn't recognise me, and wore a big hat and sunglasses. I knew that if he saw me it might affect his performance".

SWERVE

It was around this time that Frank decided to have a sex change. "I felt trapped inside my body and all that", he told us. "Deep down I wanted to wear women's clothes, read women's magazines, have tits and go out with blokes".

SKID

Frank had the operation and started life anew as Francesca. I applied for a job on the Benny Hill show. I remember at the audition Benny winked at me. I thought Oy Oy! I'm in here".

JACK KNIFE

During his three years as one of Hill's Angels, Frank had an on and off affair with Benny. "A lot of what they say about Benny is true. He was quiet, shy, generous, and he left piles of money lying about the house, often crammed into Kentucky Fried Chicken boxes or old pillow cases. But he definitely wasn't gay, and I know that for a fact".

AQUA PLAIN

Frank's affair with Benny ended as the effects of his sex change began to wear off. "I began to lose my figure, and before I knew it, I was a bloke again", he recalls.

MOUNT KERB

Having lost both a lover and a son, Frank now finds himself out of work and living on Social Security handouts. In desperation he has written to Frank Sinatra for help.

MOUNT EVEREST

"During my childhood I used to receive birthday presents from America. There was never any card or a note, just a box postmarked America. Looking back, it all begins to make sense". To this day Frank remains convinced that Sinatra is his father, and now plans a tearful re-union with the star when he visits Britain later this month for a series of sell-out concerts.

K 2

"It will be difficult knowing what to say – he probably won't even recognise me after all these years. It's going to be difficult for both of us, but I know it's something that I have to go through with".

A spokesman for Thames Television yesterday denied that Mr Hobson had ever worked on the Benny Hill Show. "In fact the whole story is a bit similar to one which appeared in a previous issue about Rolf Harris's love child", he added.

NO SEX PLEASE – WE'RE STUDENTS

Britain's universities and colleges are heading for a crisis. For as competition for brainy school leavers increases with dozens of Polytechnics now pretending to be Universities, the supply of students is slowly drying up.

And one leading academic fears the shortage of swots swarming to college is nothing to do with the courses that they offer, or new Government funding proposals for further education. He blames a lack of fanny.

K 9

Dr Seigmund Blake, head of enrolment at Fulchester Polytechnic University College of Further Education, believes that behind their academic ambitions, students have a far more important reason for going to college.

JAMIE

"They come for the birds", he told us yesterday. "After 18 years living with their parents they just want to get away from home, get their pants off and get their ends away. It's as simple as that".

LAYLA

And Dr Blake blames a change in attitudes towards sex for the fall in figures. "The women aren't playing ball these days", he explained. "It might be AIDS, it might just be fashion, but the birds aren't putting it about anymore. And as a result the fellas aren't getting any fun".

I SHOT THE SHERRIFF

Dr Blake detects a clear link between a drop in casual sex on campus and the fall in demand for university places. "In the early seventies you couldn't walk through the student union without seeing a couple at it on the floor. Everywhere you looked there were gorgeous birds, and they were real goers, I can tell you. You could spend a month of Sundays looking and still

College kipper dries up

not find a bird with knickers on. Nowadays half of them have padlocks on their fannies. The fellas must get really frustrated".

BUT I DIDN'T

According to Dr Blake applications for University places will continue to fall unless incentives can be found. "Cheap beer is all well and good, but at the end of the day it's up to the girls. If they don't start sleeping about a bit, blokes will simply stop going to college, and the whole future of the country could be jeopardized".

SHOOT THE DEPUTY

A spokesman for Newcastle Polytechnic told us that they would be changing their name to Northumbria University at Newcastle starting from next term. A male student we spoke to confirmed that girls at the college weren't even giving him a whiff. "If I don't get something by the end of the term I'm leaving", he told us.

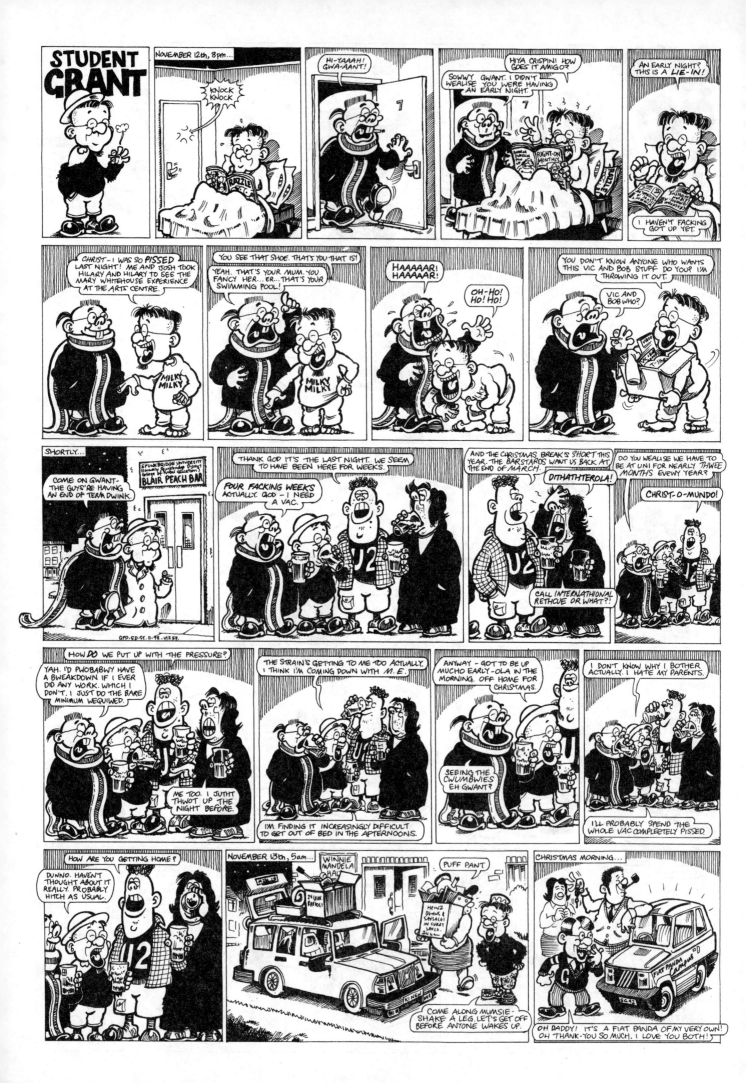

115

LETTER BOCKS

Good ☆ PRIZE LETTER
Samaritan

Could I, if I may, take this opportunity to thank the young lady with a torch who showed me to my seat in the cinema last night. If it had not been for this kind person I may well have tripped and fallen in the dark.

It is perhaps a sad reflection of modern society that out of 300 people in the cinema only one person offered to help. Nevertheless, my heartfelt thanks go to her.

Mrs D. McLean
Eaglescliffe

Under the conditions of the Fire Precautions Act 1971 I am obliged to carry out a fire drill on the letters page of this magazine every 12 months. A fire alarm will sound at some point on this page. When you hear the alarm you must stop reading at once and put the magazine down. Do not open it again until you are given the all clear signal.

J. Brown
Publisher

Cock poppycock

They say that 'size is not important'. That's nonsense. I'm a girl, and frankly we're not interested in anyone with less than 3 inches to offer. So any blokes out there with a little dick can simply forget it.

Maria Tennant
London NW3

While passing my local post office the other day I found this photograph lying on the ground. If the owner would care to write to me I will gladly return it.

C. Bonner
32 Argyle Street
Glasgow G64

How ridiculous it is supermarkets selling fruit by the pound when apples are so much heavier than grapes.

Mrs Elsa Thompson
Bishopsgate

So much for Ipswich

A few weeks after visiting Ipswich I developed a mild bladder infection from which I have only just recently recovered. A fine advertisement for the town.

C. Sugden
Bow

Why don't the British Tourist Board follow the example set by other countries and locate tourist attractions in town centres. It makes sense for the Eiffel Tower, the Statue of Liberty and the Sydney Opera House to be in easily accessible city centre locations. Why then is the Lake District over 250 miles from central London, and Edinburgh Castle a 4 hour train journey away?

E. Walsh
Fulham SW3

My wife's 'Glad' mad

My wife has gone Gladiators mad! Just the other day she came down for breakfast without touching the floor by swinging from one chandelier to another, and then proceeded to stand on top of the fridge and knock me off balance with a standard lamp. This morning she topped it all by injecting herself with steriods and developing a beard and hairy chest.

Reg Taylor
Bromsgrove

Naomi Campbell, Linda Evangelista, Cindy Crawford. Super models? Super tug boats more like it. I'd like to see what they look like at seven o'clock in the morning without their fancy "Versace" frocks or their professional "Chanel" make-up jobs.

Mr Fish
Leicester

Kitchen conundrum

We've all heard the phrase 'You get what you pay for'. Not so at my local department store. I ordered a fitted kitchen there this morning and paid for it there and then. And they tell me it won't be delivered for up to 3 weeks.

P. Hand
Kingston

Stuff your poxy towns

I'm sick of councils who advertise their poxy towns and districts on television, telling us that they're 'the place to be'. If your crappy little towns were any good in the first place, you wouldn't need to advertise them.

K. Shorter
Carlisle

* *Ding-a-ling-a-ling-a-ling
-a-ling-a-ling-a-ling-a-ling
-a-ling-a-ling-a-ling-a-ling
-a-ling-a-ling-a-ling-a-ling
-a-ling-a-ling-a-ling-a-ling
-a-ling-a-ling-a-ling-a-ling
-a-ling-a-ling-a-ling-a-ling!*

If vegetarianism is such a good idea, how come vegetarians all have bad breath and fart a lot? If God had wanted us to eat grass, he'd have made us rabbits.

Tom Higgins
Swindon

Borrowing a friend's poodle and draping it over my head I was able to pose as Brian May out of Queen and secure a prime table in a crowded restaurant.

D. Smallpiece
London E3

Remedy for Royals

These so-called problems that the Royal family are suffering at present could be solved in a day if Fergie was kicked out, Di walked out, Prince Charles shacked up with that posh bird and Edward admitted he was a queer. Then we could all get back to business as usual.

D.G.
Chatham

Is it just me or did we actually *win* world war two?

A. Marney
London SW8

Man's best friend

They say a dog is a man's best friend. Not in my case. My best friend is Neil Williamson.

C. McAlinden
Altringham

Top Tips

OAPs. Try sitting on a pile of encyclopedias next time you drive your car. That way you'll be able to see out the front window.

B. Flynn
Burnley

AND while you're on, try pushing the pedal on the right down towards the floor. This will make your car move forwards more quickly.

B. Flynn
Burnley

AVOID laziness by screwing your TV remote control to a piece of furniture at least ten feet from your chair.

Hapag Lloyd
Runcorn

OFFICE managers. Encourage primeval 'hunter-gatherer' instincts among staff by hiding nuts and berries about your office to enable them to forage for food at lunch time.

R. Villa
Argentina

CREATE instant designer stubble by rubbing syrup on your chin then sprinkling the contents of a tea bag onto it.

B. Measures
Uppingham

SILENCE your windy bottom by pulling apart your buttocks before you pump. Hey presto! No embarrassing 'fart' noise.

P. Fletcher
Wrexham

MAKE guests believe your home might be bugged by running your hands under tables and inside lampshades, then turning the shower on every time you want to speak.

C. Rumple
Balham SW12

NEVER do your shoelaces up in a revolving door.

Mr M. Adeye
Plumstead Infirmary

SOLVE the problem of disappearing Biros. Use a pencil instead.

T. Scott
BFPO 31

AVOID soiling your trousers by *not* pulling apart your buttocks when you *think* you are about to fart.

P. Fletcher
Wrexham

POLICE. Get prime seats at your local panto this year by stopping one of the celebrities as they drive home after the show full of drink. They're bound to offer you free tickets.

P. Noble
Torquay

TOP OF THE TOPS! EXCLUSIVE

Britain is top of the topping yourself league – and that's official.

Statistics show that more people than ever before are ending it all in recession hit Britain.

SUICIDE

"People have gone suicide bonkers", one leading pathologist told us yesterday. "I'm literally snowed under with stiffs. Business has never been so good".

PAINLESS

The current kamikaze craze has put Britain top of the Euro-suicide league, ahead of traditional clog popping champions Sweden. And as we get set for a harsh winter, officials fear that miserable weather could add to the problem.

BRINGS

Traditional forms of suicide such as carbon monoxide poisoning and jumping off tall things remain popular favourites. However, last year saw a dramatic decline in the number of deaths by hanging, Britain's depressives increasingly favouring the more modern approaches such as alcohol overdosing.

CHANGES

We asked a top psychologist to predict how some of Britain's showbusiness celebrities might go about killing themselves should they feel the urge to do so.

FASHION

Professor Karl Liebfraumilch of Bridlington University's Department of Suicidal Tendencies, gave us the following insight into the possible suicide techniques of the stars.

Radio One DJ **SIMON BATES** is a man who knows the value of publicity. He wouldn't waste an opportunity like this. I believe he would kill himself on live TV – possibly during a chat show – with a small handgun.

Eastenders star **DANIELLA WESTBROOK** is young and fun loving. I think she'd choose to end it all with a lethal cocktail of drink and drugs.

Prime Minister **JOHN MAJOR** lives under tremendous pressure. He would be the first Tory prime minister to top himself since the war, and I think he'd do it by jumping in front of a train.

Raunchy rock star turned nude model **MADONNA** would definitely want to go out with a bang – quite literally. I believe she would attempt to have sex with an elephant, and be crushed or split in half in the process.

Inspector Morse star **JOHN THAW** has witnessed plenty of baffling murders in his role as a TV cop. For his own demise I think he would plump for something less dramatic. I believe John Thaw would jump off a bridge.

A spokesperson for the Samaritans yesterday pleaded with any stars who are on the verge of suicide to get in touch. "We're here to help anyone who is depressed, suicidal or feels they have nowhere else to turn. And that goes for the stars of showbusiness too. Our message to the suicidal stars would be 'Don't do it – give us a call. I'm sure we can help'".

Frank Worthington

In our last issue in an article entitled 'Elephants' Ears – new theory' it was implied that former Leicester City footballer Mr Frank Worthington was unable to distinguish between Indian and African elephants.
We now accept that this was not the case, and that Mr Worthington has not at any time been confused about types of elephants.
We now wish to unreservedly withdraw our accusation, and express our sincere apologies for any distress caused to Mr Worthington and his family.

Bates – handgun   Westbrook – cocktail   Madonna – sex

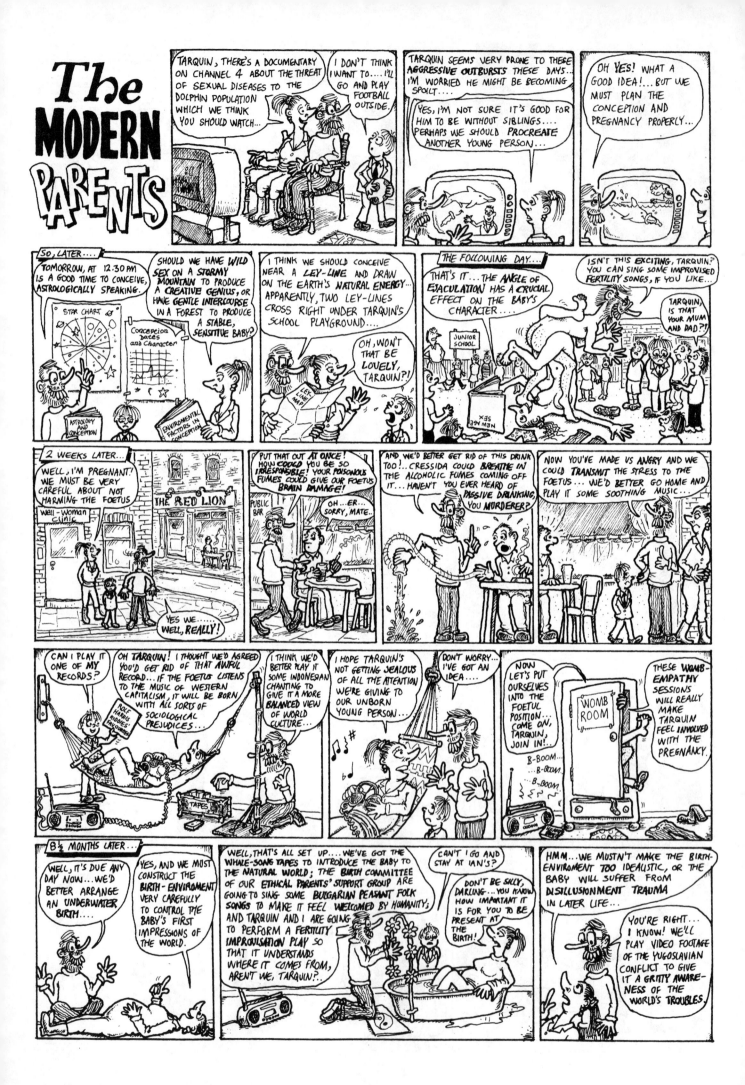

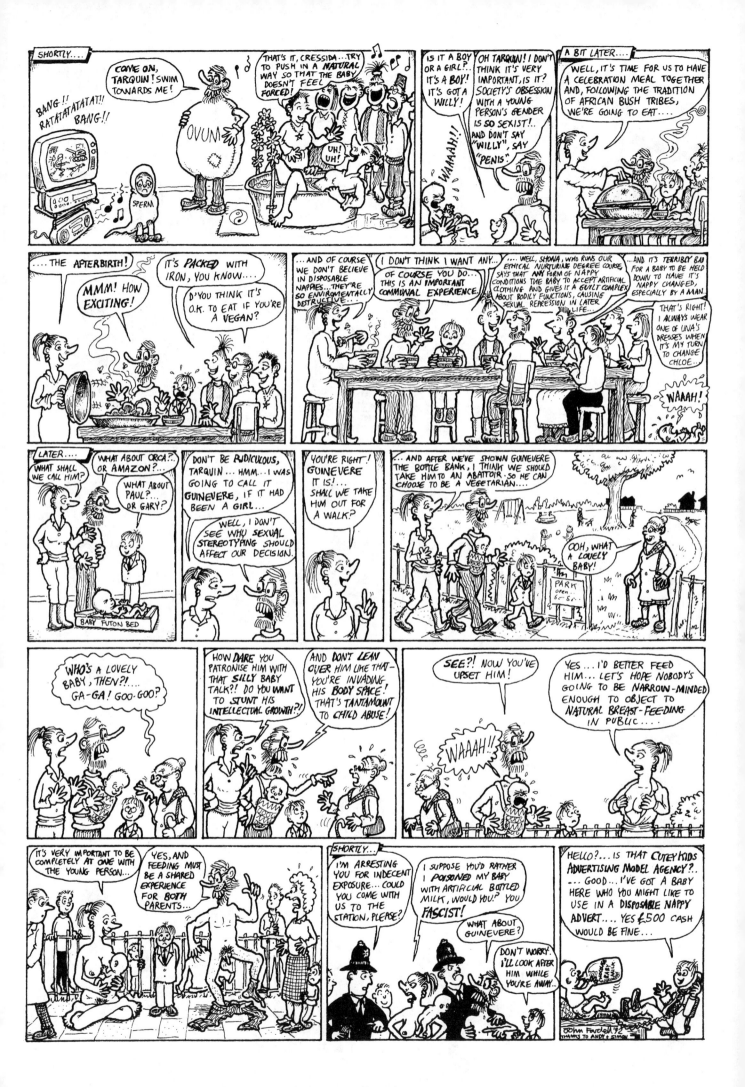

121

ZOOO 2000!

Daddy's taking us to the zoo tomorrow, zoo tomorrow, zoo tomorrow. Daddy's taking us to the zoo tomorrow, and we can stay all day.

We're going to the zoo, zoo, zoo. How about you, you, you? You can come too, too, too. We're going to the zoo, zoo, zoo.

An artist's impression of the zoo of the future in the year 2000.

SLUMPED

There was a time not so long ago when those were the words on the lips of every schoolboy and girl. But nowadays, with the advent of colour TV, multi-screen cinemas, ten pin bowling and vegetarianism, attendances at Britain's zoos have slumped, and many zoos face closure.

ADAPT

So what is the future for Britain's zoos? How will they need to adapt to survive in the fiercely competitive entertainment world of the future? We asked top animal experts Johnny Morris and Richard Attenborough to predict for us the shape of zoos in the year 2000. This is their vision of the future.

PRISON

Visitors arriving at the zoos of the future may be mistaken for thinking they were entering a prison camp. For the zoo would be surrounded by 50 foot high walls and barbed wire, and armed soldiers will accompany zoo keepers on their rounds.

HUMILIATING

Visitors will undergo humiliating body searches as they enter the gates, and any cars left unattended in the car park will be blown up by bomb disposal experts.

The reason for this tight security is that by the year 2000 loony lefties calling themselves the Animal Liberation Army will have declared war on Britain's zoos, and they will be under constant threat of terrorist attack.

DEGRADING

Inside the zoo there will be some unfamiliar sights too. For as well as old fashioned animals like monkeys, lions and bears, there will be a new attraction – space animals.

MARS

Brought to Earth in giant space rockets from far away planets like Mars and the Sun, space creatures will come in all shapes and sizes, and a variety of brilliant colours never before seen on Earth. Some will have three eyes, others ten legs. And many will be able to sort of dematerialise into silver clouds – like on Star Trek.

The bars on space animal cages will be very close together. For no matter how big the space animals may be, they will be able to change shape at will, and so they will be able to get through the smallest of gaps.

TWIX

Old-fashioned Earth animals will be updated using modern technology. Visitors will be able to play safely with remote control lions, or watch while the zoo keeper changes the giraffe's batteries. And silicon chimps will no longer have messy tea parties. Instead they'll entertain us by playing chess, listening to Radio 4 and discussing last night's viewing on Channel 4.

KIT-KAT

In the Reptile House temperatures may appear cool – but the snakes and lizards will be hotter than ever. That's because the building will revolve – using the microwave principle – heating the animals more thoroughly, from the inside, outwards, in a few seconds as opposed to minutes.

AZTEC

And as well as the hiss of snakes, there'll be the roar of mighty dinosaurs. Examples of these extinct giants will have been captured using time machines and special tranquilizer ray guns, and brought back to the future.

INCA

Meanwhile, in the Aquarium there'll be a lack of water. That's because by the year 2000 fish will have evolved and developed lungs, and clambered out of the sea and onto the land.

MAYAN

New technology will mean a dream come true for Dr Doolittle, as visitors queue up to actually talk to the

Zoo fan Johnny Austin (left) and some moon rabbits

animals. Using space technology, visitors will be able to communicate with the animals of their choice through a small decoder no bigger than a hearing aid. At the flick of a switch they will be able to talk in monkey, lion or any other animal language.

LIBERAL

And not only will we be talking to animals, in the zoo of the future we will also be having sex with them. Increasingly liberal attitudes towards sex will mean that by the year 2000 left wing councils will actually encourage beastiality in schools.

TORY

Schoolchildren will visit zoos regularly where they will learn about the important role all animals play in main-taining our environment, and they will come to respect the animal neighbours with whom we share the planet.

LABOUR

And there'll also be a working abattoir where children can fire bolts into the heads of cattle and pigs. And a special audio visual display will show the process by which animals are chopped up and turned into pies and sausage rolls.

PLAID CYMRU

Last night, former Daktari star and zoo critic Virginia McKenna blasted plans for Britain's zoos of the future. "I'm appalled by the idea of space animals being captured and brought to Earth to be displayed in this humiliating and unnatural way. Space animals should be allowed to roam free in space, on planets like Mars and the Sun", she told us.

DAFT COW
Doris's window pane in the arse

A stupid woman who bought 200 double glazed windows has called for changes in the law governing door-to-door salesmen.

Doris Twatt and her husband Frank bought the windows despite the fact that their one bedroom flat is already double glazed.

PRESSURE

They claim they were the victims of high pressure selling techniques which included:

● **KNOCKING** at their door and ringing their bell.

● **ASKING** of the Twatts wanted to buy the windows.

● **THREATENING** to call back the next day if they couldn't decide.

Eventually Mrs Twatt gave in after the salesman told her the windows would be supplied at half the usual price if she bought 200. But that still left her owing the company £280,000. And now the windows are left blocking the drive of Mrs Twatt's home.

A spokesman for BBC TV's Watchdog pro-gramme told us they were investigating the case. "Be careful when buying toys for young children this Christmas", they added. "Be on the look-out for any small, sharp or dangerous pieces which could cause a child to choke".

WIN TICKETS TO THE ZOO 2000

Here's a great competition – and a chance for you to win a free visit to one of Britain's zoos – if there's any left – in the year 2000.

IMAGINATION

All you have to do is draw what you think space animals of the future will look like. Use your imagi-nation, and the more space age your animals look the better. Colour them in with silver paint or tin foil. Then send them to 'Viz Space Animals in the Zoo of the Future for the Year 2000 Drawings competition', P.O. Box 1PT, Newcastle upon Tyne, NE99 1PT, to arrive by no later than 31st December 1999.

Another GREAT competition

We'll ask Johnny Morris, if he's still alive, to judge the competition, and the winner will receive two tickets to the zoo of the future. Five lucky runners-up will each receive a goldfish in a plastic bag.

SHAKATAK

If you'd like your pictures returned don't bother sending them in the first place. This competition is not open to members of the Animal Liberation Front, their friends or relatives. The judges' decision is final.

Mayor escapes unhurt

The Lord Mayor of Wigan escaped unhurt after aliens from Mars held him hostage in Wigan Town Hall for over 2 hours yesterday.

The silver martians landed in Wigan after their 300 foot long flying saucer had developed technical prob-lems.

DR WHO

"It was like a scene from Dr Who", said Wigan's Chief Constable Barry Hitchcock. "They were shooting at people with ray guns. It's a miracle nobody was hurt". The aliens eventually re-leased the mayor, Councillor Tom Clark, after the local

fire brigade offered to help repair their space craft. A relieved Councillor Clark later told reporters he was feeling none the worse for his ordeal. "I shall be back at work tomorrow morning at 8 o'clock sharp", he told them'.

K9

Shopping in Wigan was dis-rupted during the seige. Police closed off several streets for most of the after-noon, and local traders re-ported reduced takings.

ANSWERS

SPOT THE STAR (p.65): The mystery stars are: (a) *Sean Connery* (b) *Eric Morcambe* (c) *Ernie Wise* (d) *Mike Atherton* (e) *Liz Hurley in THAT dress.*

SPOT THE ROYAL AMERICAN TV COP (p.63): Her Majesty Queen Elizabeth the Queen Mother is disguised as private detective *Frank Cannon.*

SPOT THE BEARD (p.11): The well known celebrity *Julia MacKenzie* is wearing *Rolf Harris's beard.*

Reg on tabs.

"I smoke 'em cos I'm chemically addicted to nicotine!"

WARNING: SMOKING WHILST PREGNANT CAN LEAD TO LOW BIRTH WEIGHT.   MIND YOU, WHO WANTS TO GIVE BIRTH TO A FAT BABY ANYWAY.
Health Departments' Chief Medical Officers